# FIREFIGHTER

## —— PREPLAN ——

## The Ultimate Guidebook for Thriving as a Firefighter

## DAVID J. SOLER

### Founder of Firefighter Toolbox

## DISCLAIMER

This book is designed to provide general information regarding the subject matter covered. However, laws and practices often vary from state to state and are subject to change. Because each factual situation, fire call, and experience is different, specific advice should be tailored to the particular circumstances. For this reason, the reader is advised to consult with his or her own advisor regarding their specific situation.

The author and publisher have taken reasonable precautions in the preparation of this book and believe the facts presented in this book are accurate as of the date it was written and published. However, neither the author nor the publisher assumes any responsibility for any errors or omissions. The author and publisher specifically disclaim any liability resulting from the use or application of the information contained in this book and the information is not intended to serve as legal or professional advice to individual situations or as a certification to anyone.

The recommendations, advice, descriptions, and methods in this book or program are presented solely for educational and informational purposes. Firefighting is a dangerous activity and occupation and could cause injury and death. This information is intended for certified firefighters. The author and publisher and Firefighter Toolbox LLC assume no liability whatsoever for any loss or damage that results from the use of any of the material in this book/program. Use of the material in this book is solely at the risk of the user, even if they are a certified firefighter.

# FIREFIGHTER PREPLAN

## David J Soler

FirefighterToolbox.com
FirefighterPreplan.com

Cover Designer- Adam Thompson
Edited by - Lee Ann Obringer, EditorNancy, Madison Soler
Technical Editor - Jim Moss

Library of Congress Cataloging-in-Publication Data available upon request.

*Firefighter Preplan* /David J. Soler

Print-Paperback
ISBN-10: 0-9908442-1-8
ISBN-13: 978-0-9908442-1-1

ebook
ISBN-10:0-9908442-2-6
ISBN-13:978-0-9908442-2-8

Printed in the United States of America

# PRAISE FOR
## *FIREFIGHTER PREPLAN*

*Firefighter Preplan* is a transparent, easy-to-read book that doesn't beat around the bush. The book is all substance and no fluff, and it was written to help you become a better version of yourself. This book is a great starting point for anyone who is serious about becoming a respected firefighter. It is also a reminder of why we all do what we do: to serve others.

**Frank Viscuso**
Deputy Chief
Kearny Fire Dept. (NJ)
Author of *Step Up and Lead* and *Step Up Your Teamwork*.

*Firefighter Preplan* is an inspirational, educational, and instructional culmination of advice, ideas, and practices that will help develop or enhance anyone's career, especially a fire service career. David's passion to help make better firefighters is clearly evident on these pages. Join him in being a part of a better fire service by reading this and absorbing decades worth of information easily.

**Walter Lewis**
District Chief
Orlando Fire Dept. (FL)
FLTF-4 Search Manager

★ ★ ★ ★ ★

Wow! *Firefighter Preplan* is the type of information that is invaluable to the fire service and those who have the desire to be great firefighters.

**Bryan T. Smith**
Captain
Baltimore County Fire Dept. (MD)

This book is a must-read for every firefighter who desires to take their career to the next level. David provides a simple yet effective roadmap to success in the fire service. As a chief officer, I provide a copy of this book to every firefighter that enters my department.

**Robert C. Simmons**
Assistant Chief
Fort Leavenworth Fire Dept. (KS)

From the rookie to the veteran, this essential guidebook will provide any firefighter the knowledge and guidance necessary to thrive in the fire service.

**Josh Fannon**
Battalion Chief
Baltimore City Fire Dept. (MD)

If you are looking for a book that is honest, straightforward and has no fluff, then this is a book for you. Whether you are the new rookie, a seasoned firefighter, a driver operator or a company officer, this book is something we all should have in our toolbox. David's concept to leave this great profession called the fire service better than we found it is something we all should strive for. This book will get us started or continue us in the right direction.

**Christian J. Adams**
Engineer
18 Years in the Fire Service
City of Riverside Fire Dept. (CA)
USAR CA-TF6

I wish David had written this book 15 years ago! When I first hired on to a fulltime fire department, I had no fire or EMS experience, and a book like this would've made a fantastic map of good roads to travel on, pitfalls to avoid, and lessons to learn. Required reading for anyone, career or volunteer, who is serious about the fire service and making their way in it.

**Sean J. Wilson**
Search & Destroy Training & Tools, LLC
Royal Oak Fire Dept. (MI)

The road you're on to becoming a great firefighter is for marathoners, not sprinters! By reading or listening to *Firefighter Preplan*, you have just made the commitment necessary to move forward toward the goal of becoming the great firefighter you want to be. Kudos to the author, David J. Soler, for providing you the road map to help guide you along the way.

**Johnny Winston Jr.**
Division Chief
City of Madison Fire Dept. (WI)

★ ★ ★ ★ ★

I highly recommend *Firefighter Preplan*. The author has a wide range of experience from volunteer to career. *Firefighter Preplan* will affect all forms of firefighters from beginners to veterans with tons of experience. Two thumbs up.

**Johnny Silva**
Chief
Hayden Fire Dept. (AZ)

★ ★ ★ ★ ★

David Soler is committed to discovering—and sharing—what it means to become a great and respected firefighter. In *Firefighter Preplan*, he captures and conveys decades of experience about the actions that make great firefighters and crews. Want to be a great firefighter? Want to earn respect in the fire service? Read this book, act on these principles, and finally pass this knowledge on to those who follow in your footsteps.

**Rob Cannon,** *Lieutenant Commander, US Navy (retired)*
Fire Captain
Charlotte, Fire Dept. (NC)

This is the go-to book for aspiring firefighters and a refresher to anyone who is already in the fire service. This book helps you to understand life principles pertaining to becoming and remaining a firefighter who has passion for this work in the service of others, whether they are volunteer or paid. Great job, Dave!

**Bob Newton**
Chief,
Warren Volunteer Fire Company (CT)

*Firefighter Preplan* needs to be read by every aspiring firefighter and rookie firefighter.

Unfortunately, many firefighters do not have mentors to guide them throughout their career. Fortunately, *Firefighter Preplan* presents priceless information that every firefighter needs to know to help them achieve greatness. It is the embodiment of paying it forward.

As a fire officer who is passionate about mentorship in the fire service, I also encourage senior firefighters and officers to read this book. It contains critical information that everyone needs to pass on to the next generation to properly shape the future of the fire service.

**Jim Moss**
Lieutenant-Paramedic
Metro West Fire Protection District (MO)

Whether you are paid or volunteer, whether you've been in the fire service 5 years, 15 years, or just 5 minutes, you will get something out of *Firefighter Preplan*.

This book contains many years of experience and firefighting wisdom, relating to and affecting all aspects and ranks within a department. Required reading for anyone looking to have impact and influence throughout their fire service career.

**Jonathan Lusk**
Captain - Fresno Fire Dept. (CA)
Publisher - "Brotherhood of Fire"

★ ★ ★ ★ ★

In *Firefighter Preplan*, David J. Soler has highlighted all the necessary traits and characteristics of a top-shelf firefighter. I truly feel that this book will be a great tool in the development of our future fire service leaders.

Let this book/program jump start your fire service career and propel you into your future. It will fire you up and put you on the fast track for reaching your goals and becoming the respected firefighter you desire to be. Read it and re-read it. It will work!

**Lt. Rob Ramirez**
Dept. Training Officer,
Margate Fire Rescue (FL)
FLTF-2 FEMA USAR
Rescue Squad Officer

★ ★ ★ ★ ★

David Soler has struck gold with his newest book, *Firefighter Preplan*, which is focused on becoming all that a firefighter can be in our business. Mr. Soler's focus is to help all firefighters become well-respected and highly capable members of their department. *Firefighter Preplan* is a great guide to those ends. It's a must-read for anyone that wants to improve in the business of saving lives and fighting fires!

One of the rules to live by is to "lead from the front." *Firefighter Preplan* will help you make that happen and much more. Take the journey to improve your skills, knowledge and abilities by reading your way towards improvement. Congratulations to David Soler; he has a big hit on this hands!

**Fire Chief Dennis L. Rubin**
Author
Rube's Rules for Leadership
Rube's Rules For Survival
ChiefRubin.net

This book has timeless principles in it for firefighters. They worked 40 years ago when the Bronx was burning, they work today, and they will work 40 years from now!

**Captain Bob Farrell**
FDNY (ret.)
CEO, FirehooksUnlimited.net

*Firefighter Preplan* reminded me of the true virtues that I love about being a firefighter. Apply them and they will go a long way in helping you reach your potential as a firefighter.

**Eric J. Larson**
Line Officer (2003-2012)
Bel Air Volunteer Fire Co. (MD)
Harford County HAZMAT Team

For those wanting to see what the fire service is really about, this book is for you. *Firefighter Preplan* will really benefit new and up and coming fire-fighters or those looking to become a firefighter. It appears to have all the bases covered for becoming a respected firefighter and having a successful career in the fire service.

**Gregory May**
Captain
City of Fort Lauderdale Fire Rescue (FL)

*Firefighter Preplan* provides a great foundation to build upon throughout your career. I have gotten a lot from the book and I plan to give it to others I mentor.

**Shauna Baccus**
Saskatoon Fire Department, Saskatoon, Saskatchewan Canada
15-year fire service veteran

*Firefighter Preplan* makes an aggressive interior attack on mediocrity in the fire service. There's something in this book for every firefighter, from rookie to the senior firefighter.

**Scott Ebbert**
Lieutenant - Truck 8
Baltimore County Fire Dept. (MD)

*Firefighter Preplan* provides valuable insights and principles that all firefighters looking to become respected at their craft should read. The fire service needs to pass on our lessons learned to our firefighters and this book aims to do just that.

**Chief Patrick J. Kenny**
Director of Fire and EMS
Village of Western Springs (IL)

# The moment is coming when you will be called upon. Are you ready?

—David J. Soler

# TABLE OF CONTENTS

# For some, it's a job; for us, it's a calling.

— David J. Soler

# ACKNOWLEDGEMENTS

## This book is dedicated to

**God**, for blessing me with the calling of being a firefighter.

**Jesus Christ**, for being my Lord & Savior. All Glory to God.

**Kristen**, for your love and support

**Olivia & Madison**, For being my biggest cheerleaders and best children I could ever ask for.

All those that have poured into me, those that this book will pour into and those that I have had the honor of fighting fire with.

**My Dad**, for always encouraging me with, "You can do it."

**My Mom**, for showing me how to "never quit."

**George Cabrera**, for all the wise counsel

**Antonio Soler**, for the disciplines of success

**Firefighter Toolbox Contributors**, for pouring into the future of the fire service.

# "Great firefighters are built, one training at a time."

—David J. Soler

# SPECIAL MESSAGE FROM DEPUTY CHIEF FRANK VISCUSO

*A servant leader.* Those are the first words that I think about when someone asks me about David J. Soler. The next thought that comes to mind is that David is a man who is dedicated to God, his family, and the fire service.

**Deputy Chief Frank Viscuso**

I remember the first time I received a phone call from David inviting me onto his Firefighter Toolbox Podcast. He told me about his idea of interviewing some of the most well-known authors and leaders in our industry and sharing their thoughts with the world. He was humble and passionate, which are two valuable qualities I look for in a person.

After speaking with him for a while and hearing more about his vision, I thought about Napoleon Hill, who spent years interviewing the wealthiest people in America before writing one of my favorite books, *Think and Grow Rich*. Like Napoleon Hill, David is a sponge for knowledge—a student of our industry who is dedicated to personal growth.

Many people make the critical mistake of thinking they do not need to focus on self-education. David is not one of those people. He has spent years of his life interviewing thought leaders in the fire service, studying great firefighters and applying their principles.

He understands the power of association better than most. Associating with the right people is a key to success in life, and this book was written by a man who has spent years of his life shaping his philosophies by spending time with, and dissecting the thoughts of, the most respected leaders in the world's most respected profession. Lucky for us he packaged his findings in this book for the benefit of the men and women of today's fire service.

*Firefighter Preplan* is a transparent, easy-to-read book that doesn't beat around the bush. The book is all substance, no fluff, and it was written to help you become a better version of yourself. This book is a great starting point for anyone who is serious about becoming a respected firefighter as well as a reminder of why we all do what we do—to serve others.

The fire service cannot continue to thrive as one of the most honorable professions in the world if the men and women who take the oath and answer the call fail to understand the meaning of the word *honorable*.

Each of us has an obligation to earn the respect of our community. We all need to step up and do our part to continue the many wonderful traditions of our predecessors, as well as start new ones. This is not possible without character and integrity. It is also not possible without the right behavior and attitude.

This book will provide you with a strong foundation of timeless principles that those before us have demonstrated and now pass on to us to build upon.

There is one caveat to reading this book. It is similar to the same one that I share with every aspiring leader who picks up any great fire service tactical book, which is, "You can't throw the book at a fire and put it out."

With this book, I would slightly revise that statement to, "You will not become a great firefighter or leader simply because you read this book." The purpose of reading this book is to learn the principles and attitudes of those respected and great firefighters that have come before us that made them great and respected and then implement them into your career and life. Now it's your turn to not only read and learn these principles, but also to "Step Up" and implement them.

Any veteran firefighter would agree that within our industry, you will encounter unique challenges. This book is a great tool to help you enhance your knowledge, awareness, and understanding of some of those challenges you will inevitably stumble upon along your journey. More importantly, it will provide you with the tools you will need to overcome many of those challenges.

You must apply the information in this book, not sit on it. You must commit to becoming a better firefighter and leader. You must commit to the same thing David, myself, and so many others have done before us, which is to leave the fire service better than you found it. *Firefighter Preplan* is the starting point to help you do just that.

## Deputy Chief Frank Viscuso
Author of *Step Up and Lead* and *Step Up Your Teamwork*.

# The moment is coming when you will be called upon. Are you ready?

—David J. Soler

# INTRODUCTION

This book is about what it takes to be a great and respected firefighter and how to earn it in the fire service. It provides the priceless mental tools for our firefighter toolbox. It is best used as a guide to prepare, plan and become a better firefighter and leader.

The fire service was here long before you were here. It will be here long after you are gone. Remember to stay humble and always take care of your responsibilities like your family and your education. Now go for it!

David Soler Sr.
(My dad's advice when I was just starting out in the fire service.)

## BACKGROUND

Ever since I was a kid, I dreamed of being a firefighter. I felt the calling to be a firefighter and I also felt called to be a great firefighter, or the best I could be. Therefore, I am a student of firefighter greatness. I have been consumed by the need to seek and study the answers to the following questions:

- What does it take to be a great firefighter?
- What does it take to be a respected firefighter among other firefighters?
- How can I be respected among other firefighters both within my department and outside my department?
- Are people born with this greatness or is it learned?
- Do I have what it takes to be a great and respected firefighter?
- Are there foundational principles that great firefighters have that we can learn and embrace?
- Can others learn and implement this and can they, too, become great and respected?

After years of searching for these answers, testing what I found, sharing it with others, and seeing them become great and respected firefighters, I feel that a "map" has been discovered for all of us who have a calling to be great and respected firefighters.

*Firefighter Preplan* is the end result of my many years of interviews with great and respected firefighters from around the United States

David J. Soler, Circa 1982

and beyond—like those I share in the FirefighterToolbox podcast. (See FirefighterToolbox.com/itunes.)

Firefighters, officers, chiefs, and thought leaders from all walks of the fire service have been interviewed and studied to understand what elements and principles are common to these admired and respected fire service personnel.

*Firefighter Preplan* compiles these principles, attitudes, habits and also provides the career strategies and tactics of these admired firefighters.

Throughout the years, I've also gone on many "ride-alongs," also known as "shadowing," with numerous firefighters and officers in departments from multiple states to gather and study these principles, strategies, and tactics.

In addition, my personal experience in the fire service includes 20+ years being a firefighter in different roles such as: EMT/firefighter, pump operator, straight truck and tiller truck operator, lieutenant, and captain. This experience has been gained both as a volunteer and career firefighter in multiple states, including New Jersey, New York, and Maryland.

As a lifelong student of firefighter success, I am not here to tell you I am great or that you should bow down to me; I'm telling you to become a student of firefighter success yourself. Focus on learning the skills, attitudes, and philosophies that *Firefighter Preplan* shares as well as traits of other respected firefighters and officers you know and then implement them.

Understanding these tools will not make you respected. It's becoming the person who embodies these principles and produces the fruit of these principles that will make you respected and provide a rewarding fire service career.

The harder you work on yourself, the greater the rewards. Plant seeds of greatness in your mind, let them sprout and grow, and the bountiful harvest of respect and greatness will come forth.

This effort will produce great fruit and provide a foundation of who you are, not just what you are doing.

In fact, if you met me, you would find that I would most likely want to learn from you and ask you what it takes to be a great firefighter and leader.

*Firefighter Preplan* shares with you all the findings I have seen, tested, and discovered that are helpful in becoming a great and respected firefighter. My hope is that you too desire to become your best and implement these principles so you can fulfill your God-given ability and calling to not only be a firefighter, but also to be the best firefighter you can be—to become a great and respected firefighter.

## SO WHAT IS THIS BOOK ABOUT?

This book is about reaching our God-given potential and being a great and respected firefighter. The attitudes, philosophies, and behaviors of great and respected firefighters who have blazed a trail before us are shared here for you to learn, understand, and implement.

In addition, if you choose to "take action" and implement what is shared in this program, you will transform yourself into what others would call a great and respected firefighter.

*Beware*

There are too many *t-shirt wearing* or *paycheck-cashing* firefighters who do not have the love of the fire service nor the respect from their peers.

For them, it's just a job or they like the clout they get from "wearing the firefighter t-shirt" or saying they are a firefighter.

There is also another type of firefighter called the *2/20 firefighter*. They are the ones who seem to know it all and think they are the world's gift to firefighting. Some of them actually believe that the fire won't go out unless they are there. The 2/20 firefighter is a term used to refer to firefighters who have about 2 years in the fire service but believe they have 20 years of experience.

Beware. We are starting to see an epidemic of these three types of firefighters in the fire service and they are negatively influencing the future of the fire service. If you want to learn what great and respected firefighters do and how you can do it too, then this book is for you.

## LOVE OF BEING A FIREFIGHTER

David J. Soler Tillering Truck 15. (2013)

Like you, I love being a firefighter, and I have found others who love it too, but they are starving for good leaders and mentors to show them the ropes. They need someone to guide them on what it takes to be a respected firefighter within the fire service and the community. They aspire to be the best they can be and they love being in the fire service, but they feel the absence of a mentor or guide. They desire to have someone who can enlighten them, equip them and encourage them to their greatness. If this describes you, then this book is for you.

This book brings to you the insights, philosophies, attitudes and much more of what a great and respected firefighter is and how you can become one too. This is not all developed or thought up by me. This book comes from years of studying, implementing, and testing the insights that respected firefighters have shared.

## HOW DID THIS BOOK COME ABOUT?

I have been like a sponge for over 25 years when it comes to the fire service. I love being a firefighter and ever since I was a 3-year-old boy hanging out with my dad at the firehouse, I have been on a quest to be the best firefighter I can be.

Playing firefighter was something I consistently did as a kid, and I always dreamed of one day being the real thing. Like most aspiring firefighters, I wanted to someday have the ability to be on the nozzle and put out a fire, or rescue someone's life. I wanted to be part of a team and have a significant purpose—to be the one who someone calls on when in need.

I didn't *just* want to be a firefighter though. I wanted to be the best I could be, and I wanted to be respected as a firefighter amongst my peers. I was on a mission to find out what makes a firefighter great and respected among other firefighters, and how I could become one.

It has been 25+ years of searching, watching, studying and training with great firefighters. It has been 25+ years of working and volunteering with many different fire departments around the country, experiencing life as a volunteer and a career firefighter.

This journey includes experiencing all types of fires, rescues and EMS calls including: structure fires, auto fires, urban firefighting, suburban firefighting, rural firefighting, winter firefighting, truck and engine work, rescue and extrication work, swift water rescue, and more.

There is so much that a firefighter in today's fire service faces, and I have been blessed to experience a lot of it. I have also been blessed to be a firefighter in several states—as both career and volunteer—and had the privilege to be an officer in different departments leading brave men and women. But most importantly, I have been blessed to be around great and respected firefighters and officers from whom I was able to study and be mentored.

For that, I am ever grateful and want to do them the honor of not letting their knowledge and wisdom die with me, but to pass it on for those who will come alongside me and after me.

Through the years I have interviewed and befriended so many great and respected firefighters whom I am blessed to call my friends. Through the *Firefighter Toolbox* Podcast, and years of being a firefighter, I have interviewed hundreds (and counting) of highly respected firefighters, fire officers, and thought leaders in the fire service. In these interviews and conversations, one question that is always asked is this: *What does it take to be a great firefighter and a great leader in the fire service?*

Are you always searching for the keys to becoming a great and respected firefighter? Searching for the answer to: How can I be a great and respected firefighter? Is there a recipe? Can I teach others or share it with others?

What I have found, tested, and what has been reinforced to me over and over is what is shared in this book. When you implement these philosophies, attitudes, and disciplines, you too can achieve the same respect and greatness that those who have come before you have achieved.

## HOW HAVE I TESTED THESE PRINCIPLES?

These are the principles I used to turn low-responding, low-morale volunteer departments into highly motivated, highly respected top-responding departments, such as the Joppa-Magnolia Volunteer Fire Department's House 1 in Maryland. This department had an engine, rescue engine, brush truck, and medic and got around 1,500+ fire calls a year—which is about 4-5 fire calls per day. That is a busy volunteer fire department and they saw a lot of fire.

These principles have been used to build my career, from being hired as an EMT to becoming a firefighter, engine driver, truck and tiller driver, and becoming respected among many great and respected firefighters within two years.

These principles have been tested by others who have gotten some great results and found that when we renew our minds and transform our behaviors to those shared in this book, then respect and greatness are attracted to you like metal to a magnet.

## WARNING: BUILDING RESPECT AND GREATNESS TAKES TIME

I do have to warn you that this does take time and discipline. No one can just read a book and become a great and respected firefighter, but everyone can start today to adopt and implement these strategies, attitudes, philosophies, and disciplines and then get the honor of being a respected firefighter.

Being a respected firefighter is a journey, not a destination. It's something that we repeatedly do, and it is not a trophy. The best way I can describe it is that it's like paying rent. We have to make our monthly payments and then we get to live in this place called "respected firefighter." Once we stop making payments, we get booted out of "respected firefighter" status.

It also does not happen overnight. Being a great and respected firefighter takes time to build, like a reputation.

The attitudes, philosophies, and disciplines have to be implemented and repeated in order for us to become and remain great and respected firefighters. Once we stop training, for example, get out of shape, or are no longer able to competently do our job, we lose our place in the respected firefighter category.

## DOES IT MATTER IF I AM MALE/FEMALE? CAREER OR VOLUNTEER?

Your gender, skin color, or status as a paid or volunteer firefighter does not matter. These truths that you will learn in this book will work for you if you are willing to follow them and have them become part of who you are.

I have worked with and interviewed many great firefighters: male and female, those of all kinds of skin color and heritages, volunteer and career, American and Non-American, etc. One thing I have found in all these categories is that there are great firefighters and bad firefighters in each of these categories.

I have also found that the fire does not care whether you are paid or volunteer, it will kick your butt or worse—it will kill you. It will not go easy on you because you are volunteering. It will not be harder on you because you are female or because this is your first year or your last year. The fire is always getting tougher and it does not care about any of these things. The incidents are continuously getting more challenging, so we always need to be safe and be ready.

When you're around firefighters, one thing you know, or one thing you will find out, is that everyone is always evaluating everyone. Firefighting is a team sport or team activity. My life could very well depend on you being able to do your job on the fire ground. I may have to take a calculated risk to save a life or put myself in harm's way, and I need to know whom I can or can't count on.

## WHO ARE THE GREAT AND RESPECTED FIREFIGHTERS?

Great and respected firefighters are those who we can rely upon. The ones who know what to do and can do it effectively. Someone who will do what it takes to get the job done. Someone who knows what their limits are. Someone who is humble and respects the job of firefighting and respects the nastiness and devastation we can encounter on the fire ground, no matter if it's a "Smells and Bells" call or the "Big One."

Everybody wants to work or ride with a respected firefighter. Great and respected firefighters are at all levels. We need great and respected probies as well as senior firefighters, engineers/drivers, and officers. Great firefighters know that they need to continually be learning and honing their skills. They know they need to have mentors as well as be mentoring others. They continually train and surround themselves with other great and respected firefighters.

If you are looking to be the best firefighter you can be, if you are looking to learn from other great firefighters who have blazed the trail, if you aren't afraid of doing work, if you are willing to pay the price of success, then this book can be the guidebook or GPS to get you there.

## IS THIS ONE OF THOSE LONG AND DRAWN OUT BOOKS?

There is no fluff in this book. I give it to you straight, to the point, and in a hurry. I am not here to bore you with words or write an award-winning novel. This book is written to transfer the wisdom and knowledge of great firefighters to you in a quick and simple to understand way.

Know upfront that this book cannot give you success. I cannot guarantee you success. Success is something you earn. Success is the by-product of doing these disciplines consistently. A reputation is built on what you have done and what you continue to do and not what you know to do or what you say you will do. Respected firefighters know that it's about living it, not talking it.

David's desk where most of the interviews
were recorded and this book was typed.

There is an expression in the fire service that says, "You cannot talk the fire out." This is such a powerful statement and it has so many valuable lessons in it. At some point, it's all about what you do and not what you say. What I want you to know is that you cannot talk your way into being a great and respected firefighter. Great and respected firefighters let their actions do the talking. Their disciplines pay the rent of living in the "great and respected firefighter" home.

## LEAVE IT BETTER THAN YOU FOUND IT

A principle I learned growing up in the Boy Scouts and becoming an Eagle Scout is to leave it better than you found it. Whenever we went camping or had a meeting in a church, the mindset was the same: Leave it better than you found it. This meant we would improve something, clean something, and definitely not leave a mess behind. I don't know when my last call will be or if it has already happened, but I do know that I want to always be contributing and leaving things better than how I found them.

I hope and pray that through the brothers and sisters that have blazed this trail and set the example that has been passed on to me, that I will do a successful job of now passing all of this knowledge and experience onto you. I hope that you will use these philosophies, attitudes, insights, and timeless disciplines to be the greatest you can be and to love what you do, to love the people you serve, and to love the past and future of the fire service.

This book is my contribution back to the fire service that I love. This life that I have lived would not be as blessed if I had not had the opportunity to be a firefighter. This book is the sum of my notes focused down to the core wisdom that has been passed down to me from great and respected firefighters who are still on the fire engines today and some who have moved on to be with the Lord.

## HOW TO USE THIS BOOK

So don't just skim this book or read it once. Plan to read this over and over again so that these philosophies, attitudes, and behaviors become second nature to you. Refer back to certain strategies and tactics shared in this book throughout your career. Get the *Firefighter Preplan* audio program so you can listen to this content on your commute to work, while working out, or at other times throughout your day. Turn your smart phone into a mobile-training device. Have great trainings and inspiring audios to listen to so that you are encouraged and fed with great wisdom. (You will learn that this is one of the habits of great and respected firefighters.)

## THANK YOU FOR MAKING THE FIRE SERVICE BETTER

Lastly, I want to thank you for picking up this book. By picking up this book, you are demonstrating that you have a high personal standard of excellence. Mediocrity is not what you strive for. You strive to be the best you can be, to continually look for more resources to become better, and to contribute to your family, your fire department, your community, and the world. Thank you for your passion and effort. We need more firefighters like you that want to improve and desire to become the best they can be. If we had more like you, the fire service would definitely be at a higher level than it is today.

You are the future of the fire service. You have the opportunity to take your skills to the next level. Make the most of it. Learn these tools, philosophies, and attitudes and implement them. By living them out, respect and greatness will cling to you like metal to a magnet.

## DON'T KEEP THIS A SECRET

If you feel that these principles work and you believe in them: recommend this book. Give one to your friends, your classmates, your crew, and those in your department.

We need an abundance of great and respected firefighters. There is ample room for everyone in the fire service to be successful. Your greatness will not prevent others from greatness and their achievements will not hinder you from yours. Do not believe the lie that says, "For me to win, you have to lose." We are in a win-win game. We all can become great and respected. We all have our unique strengths and gifts that we can contribute to make the team stronger, better, and more effective. Don't forget that. Pass that on!

# BONUS:

Get this Must Read Special Report By Firefighter Toolbox.

# THE BIG 5:

## *The 5 Biggest Mistakes Firefighters Make and how to avoid them.*

Get this special report free at
www.FirefighterToolbox.com/Big5

# HOW TO READ THIS BOOK

1. Read it. Highlight it. Consume it. Study it. Repeat.

2. Treat this like a map book or guide book and study it and refer back to it often. Highlight, circle, or star sentences, phrases, and key points that you want to learn and implement. Write notes in the book and dog-ear pages for future reference.

3. Decide on what you are going to implement from the key ideas from each chapter. Write out an action plan and make index cards with the key ideas you want to learn and memorize.

4. Share quotes and content on social media that strike you or resonate with you to encourage others. Please use #FFPreplan.

5. Get the audio program so you can take in the information audibly, which will help you retain the information.

6. Study the book with a mentor. This provides a great way to learn about their experiences.

7. Look to mentor someone. After you start implementing and getting good results, be willing to share with other up-and-coming firefighters. This will also help you by reinforcing what you have learned.

8. Read the action plan at the end of each chapter to get you started with implementing that strategy or tactic. Look to do those exercises or add them to your plan.

# *FIREFIGHTER PREPLAN* DEFINED

## Definitions:

### Firefighter -

A **firefighter** is a *rescuer* extensively trained in *firefighting*, primarily to extinguish *hazardous fires* that threaten property and civilian or natural populations, and to rescue people from dangerous situations, like collapsed or burning buildings or crashed vehicles. -Wikipedia

### Preplan [prē plan]
*verb*

1   Preplan is to plan something out in advance or to determine in advance how something should go. -Yourdictionary.com

### Firefighter Preplan -

To plan and achieve a successful and rewarding firefighter career, being ready for the challenges, storms, hardships, trials and tribulations one will encounter as a firefighter and thrive through them to selflessly assist and aid their communities, fellow firefighters and the fire service; While continuing to bring honor to the fire service like those that came before us did and to leave the fire service better than we found it to those who will come after us.

# Be the one to take control of the situation and change it for the better.

— Battalion Chief Joe Turner
Firefighter Toolbox Podcast, Episode 001

## STRATEGY #1

# ALWAYS TAKE
# 100% ACCOUNTABILITY
# 100% OF THE TIME

*An unmotivated firefighter is like a*
*flashlight with dead batteries. Both are dead*
*weight until they get recharged.*

## 100% ACCOUNTABILITY

One day, a new recruit named Omar showed up late.

As Omar walked into the classroom, the instructor called out, "You're late."

Recruit Omar replied, "The alarm clock didn't go off and so I woke up late, sir. But I'm only 5 minutes late."

The instructor, being quite intrigued and disgusted by his new recruit's attitude, asked, "Who's responsibility is it for you to be here: the alarm clock or you?"

"Um, well," said Recruit Omar hesitantly, "mine."

"Did you plan for your alarm clock to fail at some point?" questioned the instructor.

"No, sir. I guess I didn't," responded Omar.

"What would happen on the fire ground if you were given the job to provide vertical ventilation on a dwelling and you went to get the saw and it didn't work? Do you just not vertically ventilate? Do you just let the team down because everything didn't go as planned?" questioned the instructor. "It is totally unacceptable for you to be late. You are getting written up. You are lucky you are not fired this instant," the instructor scolded.

Then the instructor addressed the class, "Great and respected firefighters are not late. What can you do to ensure you are never late?"

Recruit Omar thought for a second and hesitantly stated, "Maybe have a second alarm clock?"

"Great idea!" The instructor encouraged. Then he questioned, "What if the power goes out in your house?"

"Have a battery-powered alarm clock," Omar retorted.

"Great idea," encouraged the instructor, and then he continued the questioning with, "What if your car doesn't start? What if your car has a flat? What if the roads are closed? Thinking of these scenarios and planning to overcome them is what we call *contingency planning* or *pre-planning*. This concept is extremely important to understand and must be adapted immediately to your life to be successful as a firefighter.

"When someone calls 9-1-1 and the fire department doesn't show up, the caller does not want to hear that 'the alarm bells didn't work so nobody knew to respond.' No, when someone calls 911, they don't want excuses; they want us to be ready, to be properly equipped, and to respond immediately."

One of the most important and basic steps a firefighter can do to demonstrate 100% accountability is to never be late. There are many other things a respected firefighter has to learn, but learn this lesson quickly and understand the importance of it: being 100% accountable is important in all levels of the fire service.

When we do not perform our role or job on the fire ground, people get hurt or killed. Giving an excuse does not make it acceptable. It's a "yes" or "no" box to check. Either you did the job or you didn't. We do not have time for your excuses. Frankly, it really does not matter, because at the end of the day, it's got to get done.

The first step is being 100% accountable for yourself, then you may have the privilege and responsibility of being 100% accountable for your crew or an apparatus.

Respected firefighters take 100% accountability for themselves, their responsibilities, and their crews if they are in a leadership position.

## 100% ACCOUNTABILITY 100% OF THE TIME

Like the scenario above, I personally have several alarm clocks (and I know a lot of other firefighters who do as well). Now we have smart phones with alarms, but I still have a battery-powered alarm clock and an electric-powered alarm clock. Sometimes, I even have someone call me or text me to make sure I am up and on my way if I have concerns of oversleeping.

Why? Because I need to make sure I am there. It's my responsibility. I have back-up plans and contingency plans to make sure I get the job done, which in this case is showing up early to work or wherever I need to be.

This is something that must be learned early on in recruit school. One thing that will get you relieved of your duty or fired quickly is being late as a firefighter. It demonstrates unreliability and a lack of discipline and accountability.

If they can't trust us with the little things like getting there on time, how can they trust us with the big responsibilities like carrying out an assignment on the fire ground?

Respected firefighters take 100% responsibility 100% of the time. They think about what could go wrong, and they have a back-up plan or two (or three).

## OWN IT

Another attitude respected firefighters have is the "own it" attitude. Whenever I do  something wrong or make a mistake, I own it! It's all mine.

Respected firefighters know that nobody is perfect, including themselves. I know that no matter how much pre-planning I do or how focused I am, there will come a time when I mess up. Instead of making excuses, I own it. I take full responsibility and I take the punishment that goes with it.

I accept the blame quickly, make the adjustment to correct it, take the punishment accordingly, and move on. Nobody has gone through the fire service without messing up. Yes, it's embarrassing and definitely hurts the ego, but the truth is, it will happen. The key is to own it. Others will either already know you messed up or they will figure it out eventually. So the best thing to do is own it.

When we own it, we take the responsibility and acknowledge that we made a mistake. We take corrective measures to ensure it doesn't happen again and then we know that it is behind us. People will be more quickly to forgive and forget when you own it.

This is one of the most important attributes of respected firefighters and it is what yields them praise from others. You'll hear things like:

"Yeah, he messed up, but everybody does. At least he owned up to it and fixed it."

47

"We can count on her, because she's not afraid to admit to a mistake and fix it"

"Wow, that's admirable that he admitted it. Not many people would have. That's impressive."

So remember:

Respected firefighters take 100% responsibility 100% of the time. They think about what could go wrong and they have a back-up plan or two or three. Then, when they do mess up, they own it and take corrective measures to ensure it doesn't happen again.

Lastly, a respected firefighter gives the glory to the crew and the team, not themselves. They accept the compliment, but share it with their crew/team.

For example, the chief comes to you and says, "Great job on the nozzle today. You held that fire to just two rooms. It could have very easily taken the whole floor and even the second floor."

"Thank you, Chief. I appreciate the kind words and I know that it was not just because of me. FF Sally did a great job feeding me the line, and pump operator Bruce had the water to me perfectly, and I know the captain had our overall strategy and safety under control, so it gave me the confidence to get in there quickly and do my job. It's great being a part of this team. I am glad to be able to contribute."

Respected firefighters take 100% responsibility 100% of the time. They own their mistakes and share the glory when things go well.

# ACTION PLAN

1. Always take 100% accountability.

2. If you don't know how it's your fault, humbly ask yourself or someone else whom you trust:

   - I am better than this, so what can I do better in this situation?
   - How can I prevent this from happening again?
   - How do others own this responsibility?
   - What is it that I can learn and/or change about myself from this situation to make sure this doesn't happen again?

**Is there any greater love than to lay down one's life for one's friends or a stranger? I don't think there is.**

STRATEGY #2

# SHOW INITIATIVE

*You can watch and wait for a crop or you can plant one. Which one will give the higher percentage of reaping a crop?*

# INITIATIVE

A new, up-and-coming firefighter knew she wanted to be the best she could be. She didn't want to just wait for someone to hopefully come along and tell her what she would need to do to get better or what skills she needed to develop and master.

So she sat at the kitchen table and wrote down a bunch of skills she thought would be very beneficial to develop. She then looked up classes that were available for training on those skills. (This was the start of her *training journal.*)

At that time, an officer walked in the kitchen and she asked the officer, whom she respected, about some of the items on her list. She asked her officer if these items were important and what that officer did to personally develop those skills and abilities.

She took notes on what the officer was telling her. She picked up some great nuggets of wisdom. She then asked if they could train on some of these items and also if the officer knew of some other opportunities for training on these skills.

Again, she took notes and continued with her development plan.

Who in your fire department do you respect who has an advanced skill or expertise that you could learn from?

Are you waiting for them to ask you to train or are you going to ask them about their skill or expertise?

Do you have poor leadership in your fire station? If so, where else can you find officers and senior firefighters whom you do respect?

Don't let your current situation determine your future outcome. If there is an obstacle, go over it, go around it, go under it, or grab a ladder and climb over it. Take the initiative and demonstrate your desire to become a better firefighter and leader.

. . . . . . . . . . . . . . . . . . . . . . . . . . . . .

*Don't let your current situation determine your future outcome. If there is an obstacle, go over it, go around it, go under it, or grab a ladder and climb over it. Take the initiative and demonstrate your desire to become a better firefighter and leader.*

. . . . . . . . . . . . . . . . . . . . . . . . . . . . .

If you do this, then two things will happen. First, the great firefighters will take notice and look to help you. Second, the not-so-good firefighters will mock you and discourage you. It will be easy for you to find who is a great firefighter and who isn't by how they respond to your initiative. Once they've shown you their true colors, befriend the great ones.

Great firefighters take the initiative. There are so many valuable resources, skills, abilities, and knowledge that we have access to if we just look. In fact, right in your own firehouse or department, I can 99.9% guarantee that there is some kind of resource that won't cost any money that you can tap into to learn and take your skills to the next level.

Great firefighters know this and continually show initiative for achieving their goals and becoming a better firefighter and leader.

# THE TRAINING JOURNAL

As mentioned in the previous example, it is extremely valuable to have a training journal. A training journal can be a spiral notebook, a 3-ring binder, or even an electronic app like Evernote™.

The training journal is used to collect ideas, notes, nuggets of wisdom, items to share, class notes, podcast notes, blogs to read, podcasts to listen to, class schedules, etc.

We learn much more by writing than we do by just listening or reading. So, when we write notes and ideas, the process helps us retain much more of the content.

**Div. Chief Johnny Winston, Jr. hitting the books, setting the example and showing initiative. Studying at the station is a great use of our station down time.**

Courtesy: of Div. Chief Johnny Winston, Jr. - FirefighterToolbox.com

The journal also works as a refresher from classes we took or notes we have taken. This will help us share key ideas that we learn and use.

Having this journal allows us to stay organized. We can even write about calls or experiences we had in the journal.

Even today, I go back to my notes to review certain items like HAZMAT nuggets or pump-operator equations. I also use it for teaching from my own experiences and even writing this book.

# ACTION PLAN

1. Start your training journal today!

   Old school = a notebook or a 3-ring binder
   New school = Evernote™ or something similar

2. Get either a notebook or app like Evernote™.

3. Have this with you at all trainings and take notes and categorize your notes.

4. Write questions that you have, then refer to it at trainings and at the kitchen table at the firehouse and get the answers.

4. List three or more goals you have and five items to do to get you closer to that goal. Then schedule it in your calendar. Show initiative and don't wait.

# Tell me about the five people you spend the most time with, whose opinion you value most, and I can tell you what's important to you and where your life is headed.

— David J Soler

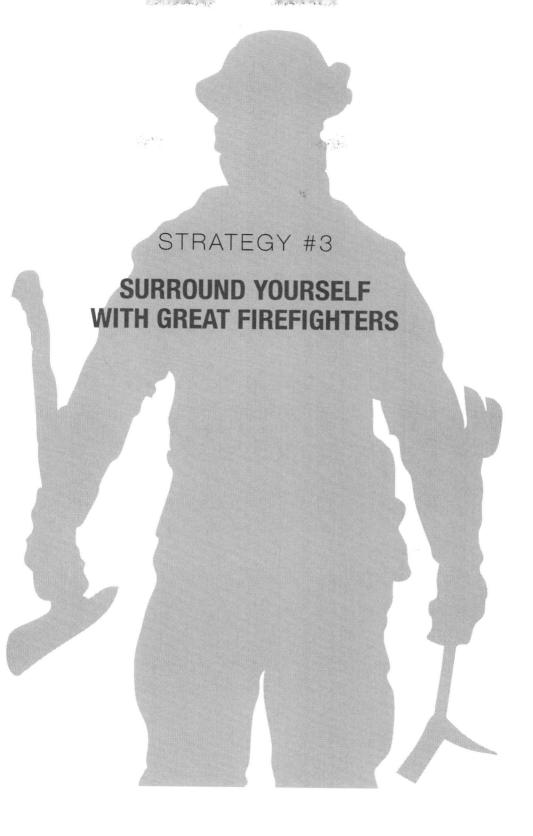

STRATEGY #3

# SURROUND YOURSELF WITH GREAT FIREFIGHTERS

David J. Soler, Brian Griffin, Capt. Bryan T. Smith pictured.

Surrounding yourself with other great firefighters is an
easy way to learn more and get better as a firefighter.

*Courtesy: Author and the Walford Road fire.*

It is said that we become like the five people we surround ourselves with
by spending the most time with them and letting them influence our
decisions.

If we hang out with people that go to the bar every Friday night, there is an
extremely high chance that we will be going to the bar with them on Friday
night. If we hang out with those who are working out and exercising, we
will be influenced to do the same.

This is an extremely powerful lesson. If you simply start befriending and
spending time with those you want to be like, then you will easily start
becoming like them. The people whom we look to for validation and

influence are those we are friends with. Those we want to emulate and be associated with are those that we most want to be like.

The litmus test is to ask ourselves this question to decide if we want to keep our current group of friends and if that group of friends is a positive influence on us:

▶ Would I want to change places with this person today?

Now, nobody is perfect, so no matter who we associate with, they will always have faults just like we do. The questions are (figuratively speaking):

▶ Where are they headed?
▶ Do I want to go where they are headed?
▶ Do their morals and philosophies align with mine or positively influence me?

If you are not liking the direction, it may be time for a change. Start to spend less time with them and find others who will positively impact you and are going in the direction you want to go.

In some cases, we have to work with some individuals or officers that we do not want to emulate. Be respectful of them, but do not take their advice and do not let them speak into your life. We all need and desire friendships, so choose to have friends and influences that are healthy, honest, positive, and encouraging. The key is to be aware of who these influences are and make the conscious choice.

**For more on this topic,**
**check out the Division Chief Walt Lewis Interview:**
FirefighterToolbox.com/053

# ACTION PLAN

▶ Listen to Firefighter Toolbox Podcast 053.

▶ Regularly evaluate or complete a report card on your associates.

▶ Make changes as needed.

STRATEGY #4

# EARN RESPECT WITH YOUR ACTIONS

# Respect is earned not given. Earn it by doing, not talking. Stop talking because I hear all I need to hear in your actions.

— David J. Soler

# RESPECT

Great firefighters have a tremendous amount of respect because they have earned it. The first step in earning respect is to give respect to those who deserve it. Give respect to those who have come before you and those who have blazed the trail.

## WHO AND WHAT DO THEY RESPECT?

They respect the firefighters who came before them, and they respect the ones that will come after them. They respect the past and the future. They respect the one in the front seat and they respect the one in the back seat.

They respect the one who has been doing it for 20 years who blazed the trail and they respect the one who has been doing it for two years for the trail they will blaze in the future.

They respect the ones we serve. They respect a job well done. They respect the fire and all it can do. They respect other fire departments and other first responders.

They understand that firefighting involves a team working for one goal. They know that they cannot do it alone, no matter how strong or knowledgeable they are.

They respect themselves and hold themselves accountable. They respect others and hold others accountable.

They are always looking to encourage and build up the ones around them and they are always grateful and honored for others encouraging them.

To get respect, they know they must give it and earn it. They earn it by continually doing the respectable thing. We cannot build a reputation or earn respect by talking. It's by doing that we build a reputation and then earn the respect of our peers, officers, fellow firefighters, mutual aid companies, departments, etc.

Here are some behaviors that, in combination and done consistently over time, earn respect.

- Showing up early
- Getting and having your gear ready
- Checking your SCBA
- Knowing where the equipment is on the apparatus that you're riding
- Being proficient in the applicable skills
- Being respectful
- Looking to help others and doing so when needed
- Being ready when called upon
- Being willing to work
- Being willing to learn and share
- Being prepared
- Continuing to enhance your knowledge, skills and abilities
- Being well-mannered and even-tempered
- Being responsible
- Not avoiding work
- Not making others' jobs more difficult
- Being a part of the solution and not the problem
- Not causing trouble
- Not causing anybody to have to write paperwork because of you

These are just a few specifics, but I think you are getting the point and can make a more detailed list for your specific job/department.

The key is to know them and then do them over and over. Over time, others will develop respect for you and your abilities because of you continually demonstrating them.

> You can't talk a fire out and you can't talk your way to a respectable reputation.

Know this and demonstrate it daily by doing the work that earns you the respect of others.

. . . . . . . . . . . . . . . . . . . . . . . . . . . . .

*Once achieved, great firefighters maintain the respect of others with integrity. Being honest with themselves and others builds respect (as you have read throughout this book in many examples). One of the fastest ways to lose that respect is when you start lacking integrity and honesty. This happens when we don't want to take accountability for our actions or mistakes. (i.e. - Covering up something or not being honest with others or ourselves).*

. . . . . . . . . . . . . . . . . . . . . . . . . . . . .

# ACTION PLAN

▶ Make a list of the specific respectable habits you want to incorporate into your fire service career.

▶ Write them on an index card and/or have the list in an app like Evernote™.

▶ Review this list as a checklist to perform during each and every shift. If you're a volunteer, then make it a weekly checklist (or whenever you are at the fire station).

▶ Track your progress and even make it a friendly competition with yourself. See how many consecutive days you can do your checklist or how many items a day you can do consistently.

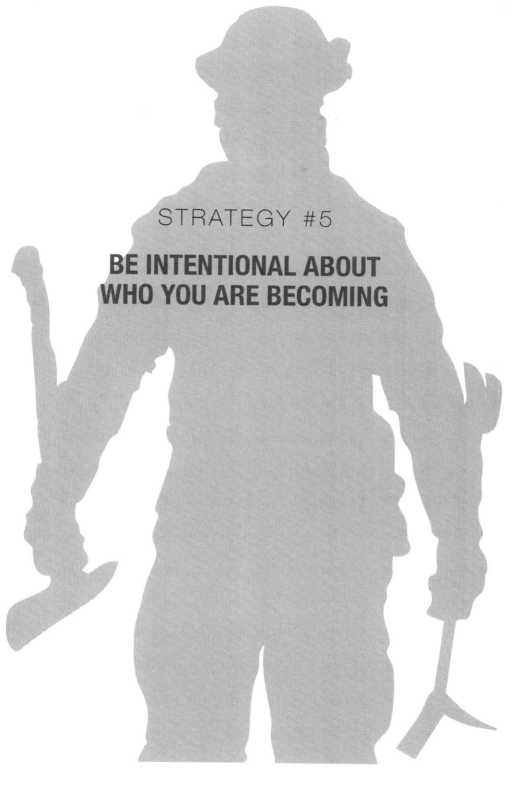

STRATEGY #5

# BE INTENTIONAL ABOUT WHO YOU ARE BECOMING

# BE AWARE OF WHOM YOU ASSOCIATE WITH AND INVEST YOUR TIME WITH.

Living in the Baltimore area and being a firefighter there, I found out pretty quickly how passionate people are about blue crabs. Old Bay crabs are something that I think everyone eats there. Crabbing season was something always talked about in the fire station and getting a bushel of crabs and some beer is the sign of a great time of fellowship. If you're ever in the Baltimore area, you will definitely want to experience eating Old Bay crabs.

Now, what most people don't know about crabs is something we can learn a lot from as we start to grow as people and adopt these philosophies, attitudes, and behaviors.

One of the most common ways to catch crabs is to use crab pots. A crab pot is a cage that has an opening at the top. The cage sits at the bottom of the bay with a rope attached so it can be pulled back to the boat or dock or wherever it's being deployed from.

Bait, like a piece of chicken, is tied inside the cage at the bottom. The crab pot is deployed to the bottom of the bay and is left there. Eventually, a crab, and most times many crabs, goes into the cage to eat the bait.

It starts hustling in there and feasting on the big piece of meat. The other crabs see or smell it and they too start piling in. Eventually, if left there long enough, the bait runs out.

Most would think that the crabs would just leave the crab pot when they are done eating, but they do not.

There are two theories to why the crabs don't leave the trap. Remember that the opening of the crab pot is still open. It's not a trap door. The way in is also the way out.

The first theory is that the crabs can't find their way out. These crabs have piled into the crab pot and cannot find their way out.

The second theory is that some of the crabs in the pot won't let the other crabs leave. Once one starts trying to leave the crab pot, another crab will pull it back into the trap. So they all stay in there and wait for the person to pull the trap from the water and have them for dinner.

Crabs are also known to cannibalize each other. If the traps are left there too long, the crabs will kill each other and the biggest one usually wins.

What's the point to this story? Don't be a crab and don't hang out with crabs because you're going to end up dead. Therefore, be careful about who you associate with.

Are your friends and mentors in the fire service people who encourage you?

If you do what the others in your station/shift do, will you be a better firefighter and person?

If I came to your station with my video camera and recorded what you and your crew did for the last four shifts, would it inspire and motivate other firefighters?

By looking at the video footage that I recorded, who would want to join your crew?

Athletic firefighters hang out with athletic firefighters. Encouraging firefighters hang out with other encouraging firefighters. Respected firefighters hang out with and work with other respected firefighters. They don't want to work with or hang out with the egotistical firefighters who think they know it all. They want to be around firefighters who take 100% responsibility. Therefore, if you aspire to be a respected firefighter and be accepted by admired firefighters, you need to do the things respected firefighters do.

Now, there are times when we get put on a shift that isn't a good fit. It may be the old timers' shift where they are just waiting to retire and watching the proverbial retirement clock. You may be in a situation with an officer who is a poor leader and is not consistent. If this is the case, and these situations do happen in a career more often than not, then make it a temporary situation and look to transfer.

Get on a shift with officers you want to emulate. Get on a shift with people who are encouraging and passionate about what they do. Do your research before you go to that department or to that shift. Learn from others who have worked with them. Learn about their reputations. Do a ride-along with them or train with them in order to get to know them. If that's not possible, look to do a shift exchange or work for someone on that shift/station to get a feel for what it's like to work with them.

Don't just go blindly into the trap like the crabs. Do your research. Great firefighters know that being on a bad shift can drain us very quickly, so an ounce of prevention is worth a gallon of medicine.

Evaluate who you spend the most time with and think about whether you would want to change places with them. Do you want to be like them? If the answer is "no," then start looking for new friends and mentors who you want to be more like. Then start being friends with them.

If and when you start hanging out and working with other respected firefighters, you now will have positive peer pressure to be a respected firefighter. Days will come when you don't feel like training. Fortunately, they will be there to make sure you train.

When you have not gotten your workout in and are having a "lazy day", they'll be there to encourage you to work out.

When I started training for triathlons, the #1 thing I knew I needed to get was a training buddy who was passionate about the goal. I was blessed to find Todd. We set up our training schedules so that we could train together 90-100% of the time. We both knew that if we expected each other for a training session, positive peer pressure would get us through the days when our brains started giving us reasons to skip out.

Well, one Friday after working all day, I was tired. I just wanted to go home, eat, watch a movie, and go to sleep. As I was thinking about it, I got a text from Todd saying, "I'll see you at 5:30 for 25 miles, right?"

When I saw that text, it brought a smile to my face, because I saw this rule working for me. I responded to the text message with, "You better bring your A-game 'cause I'm tired of waiting for you." That's bicycle talk for, "Bring it 'cause we're on."

I thought to myself, *Wow. What if my friend had wanted to go out and get some beer and wings?* If this had been the case, I probably would have gotten a text saying, "Meet me at the bar at 5:30 for happy hour." Instead, we were both into triathlons and interested in influencing each other to achieve our goals.

This is the same with being a great firefighter. Other respected and great firefighters will positively influence you to keep doing the things that great and respected firefighters do. These little nudges are the things that keep us going over the long term.

It is virtually impossible to think you can hang out with and surround yourself with slackers or firefighters who are not respected without having it influence you. Always hang around other respected firefighters for that positive influence.

# ACTION PLAN

▸ Who are the top five people you associate with?

▸ If you were to be more like them, would that make you a more respected firefighter?

▸ Who are respectable firefighters you would like to befriend?

▸ What are some ways you can spend more time with them? (Examples: Can you train with them? Work on their shift? Take a class with them? Workout with them?)

▸ List the activities that inspire you while on shift.

▸ Make a checklist and start following it when you are on shift.

▸ Start surrounding yourself and spending more time with those who inspire you.

# Great firefighters aren't born, they're built one training at a time.

— David J. Soler

STRATEGY #6

# TRAIN FOR CONFIDENCE AND COMPETENCE, NOT ARROGANCE

# TRAIN FOR CONFIDENCE AND COMPETENCE, NOT ARROGANCE

Respected firefighters have a high personal standard and a very small ego. They know that it takes a team to be successful on the fire ground and that the chain is only as strong as its weakest link. So they hold themselves to a high personal standard to be a strong link in the chain.

Highly respected firefighters invest their time and energy in training. Training includes taking classes, getting certifications, getting degrees, re-certifications, continuing education credits, hands-on training, practicing their skills, drilling on a regular basis to keep their skills sharp, and reading up-to-date articles on new strategies and tactics of the ever-evolving science of firefighting.

They do this so they can contribute more, become more valuable to the team, and to be the best firefighter and leader they can be. It's a personal standard and not something they do to be better than anyone else. They understand that firefighting is a team sport and we cannot do it alone. They also know that taking a class, listening to a training podcast, reading up on new strategies

David J. Soler training on vehicle stabilization and extrication. Leading a training class is a great way to build your confidence in that skill set.

and tactics, improving their proficiencies in the field, etc., can make them a better asset to the team. The better the team, the more effective and productive they are on the fire ground and in the firehouse.

The more effective and productive we are as a team, the more lives are saved! The goal is this: To save lives, to mitigate emergencies, to preserve property, and to do it in the most cost-effective way possible to save money for the communities we serve. The more we do this individually and as a whole, the more we fulfill our oaths as firefighters.

## No one puts a fire out by themselves.

—Battalion Chief Mike Meyers, FDNY
   Firefighter Toolbox Podcast, Episode 012

Unfortunately, we see a lot of people in the fire service train and do things out of arrogance. They have low self-esteem and want to prove their self-worth by knocking others down. These firefighters desperately want respect and to be great but are going about it the wrong way. Choose not to be like them.

Let's build ourselves up by training and developing confidence in our ability to do the skills of this job. Whether it is tying knots, deploying an attack hose line, or searching a second floor, all these skills and many more are important. Great firefighters train on these and all skills so that when they are called upon to do that job, they can confidently do the job.

By training on all of these skills, others will notice and they will respect you for it. This continual process builds respect among your peers. This also builds our confidence to know we can do the job when called upon. You won't have to be intimidated or scared of what others will think or say. You won't have to hide on the fire ground or do things to delay in an effort to avoid the job you were needed to do.

When I was a new firefighter, I remember quite vividly how certain firefighters would take a lot longer to get geared-up and on the unit than others. I discovered that these "senior firefighters" and "officers" weren't proficient in the skills and abilities needed for certain types of calls. So, instead of recognizing that and training on those skills and abilities, they just "stalled" on getting out the door or getting to the scene so they wouldn't be used or called upon to do the job.

(Figuratively speaking, we call this behavior "hiding on the fire ground.")

As a new and up-and-coming firefighter, I was hungry for action. I wanted to put my training to the test and to practice my skills and abilities on the fire ground to help someone. It was disappointing to see these senior firefighters and officers behave this way, as they weren't fooling anyone but themselves.

Let's not be like that. Others may not call us out on this, but the more honest we can be with ourselves and the more we are willing to train on these areas of improvement, then the more effective we can be as firefighters and leaders.

. . . . . . . . . . . . . . . . . . . . . . . . . . . . .

*The more you sweat on the training ground,*
*the less you bleed on the fire ground.*

—Frank Viscuso, Step Up and Lead

. . . . . . . . . . . . . . . . . . . . . . . . . . .

*What skills do you need to know, but are not confident in? Which of your*
*skills are a little "rusty" from lack of use or training?*

Make a list of the skills and jobs that you need to know but are not yet
confident that you can do. This lack of proficiency could be because you
have not needed these skills in years or because you just forgot. It could also
be because you never mastered them or had the ability to train on them,
or maybe you've just never been taught those skills. Whatever the reason,
it does not matter. What matters is identifying those skills and abilities
and making a list of them. Then list them in order of the importance and
urgency in which you need to become competent in them.

Develop a plan to start becoming proficient in those skills. Is it a class you
need to take? It is a book you need to read? Is it a video you need to watch?
Is it meeting up with other firefighters or officers who are very proficient
in those skills and asking them to give you some pointers and maybe drill
with you on them?

Great firefighters are not prideful in an egotistical way. They do have a
high personal standard for excellence, but they are not afraid to admit
to themselves that they need to learn something or that they are not as
proficient as they feel they need to be in a certain skill or ability.

So don't be so prideful that you are afraid to ask for help or pretend to know something you don't because you are afraid of what others will think. Most likely they don't know the same thing, or they don't know other things that you are proficient in. In most cases, they will be glad to train with you because they know that it will make them even more proficient in their skills.

Again, firefighting is a team sport. We are only as strong as our weakest link on the fire ground. So, first we strive to train and be proficient in our skills and abilities, then we train with our crew so that we are proficient working as a team and complement our strengths and stabilize our weaknesses.

We also train with other crews/departments/mutual-aid companies so that we can: learn from each other, get to know each other, and train on how to operate and work together as a team—again, so that we are confident that we can accomplish our mission as a team.

Remember, most people don't like to admit their weaknesses. Most other companies don't want to train with you if all you do is point out their weaknesses or "show them up." Be humble, be willing to learn, and be willing to teach. These are attributes of great firefighters and leaders in the fire service.

If we identify areas of improvement for ourselves and our team and then work on building proficiency in those areas, we will become better firefighters and leaders.

You will also start seeing other people's weaknesses. Be willing to mentor and teach in a non-threatening way. Invite them to train with you and then give your feedback on the training. Share your knowledge in a humble way, without a "know-it-all" attitude.

Teaching your skills and abilities to others is the way to achieve mastery, so make it a point to teach and share your skills and abilities. Make it a point to train consistently and to train with others. This will increase your confidence by knowing you can perform these skills and abilities. You will be rewarded for it and others will as well.

In all fire departments, we have our "bread-and-butter" (high-frequency) calls and then we also have low-frequency calls. These low-frequency calls may include drafting operations for some urban firefighters or high-rise fires for suburban firefighters. Great firefighters have a plan to train on such skills at least annually to maintain proficiency.

If you're in a leadership position, set up trainings to review these types of calls and the skills/abilities necessary to stay confident and proficient. If you're not an officer, "step up" and suggest to those who are how great it would be to train on those types of calls. That way, you all are ready when called upon.

# ACTION PLAN

▸ List 3 skills to become proficient in or to refresh on.

▸ Find others who are willing to train on the same areas.

▸ Set up 1-5 training sessions to include the technical knowledge and the practical evolutions/ training of these skills.

▸ Repeat as necessary.

STRATEGY #7

# BUILD A RESPECTED REPUTATION

## LET'S EXAMINE HOW A REPUTATION FOR BEING LAZY OR A BAD REPUTATION IS BUILT FIRST.

To build a lazy reputation, simply do lazy things over and over. Or, to build a bad reputation, simply do bad things over and over. You'll find that you will earn a lazy reputation a lot quicker than you will earn a "respected firefighter" reputation. Building a reputation as a respected firefighter takes a lot more time, and the stage of your career does not matter.

So a key difference is that it will take longer to build a reputation of respect than it will to get labeled as "lazy" or "no good." You can be lazy only a few times and get labeled as "lazy," but you will have to do the respected things for a longer duration before you start to earn the respect of others.

## BE GREAT AT EVERY LEVEL

### Successful firefighters invest in themselves.

—David J. Soler
Firefighter Preplan

*Grow wherever God plants you!*

Your time on the job isn't always a factor. Remember, you can be a great rookie firefighter. You can be a great senior firefighter, you can be a great driver, and you can be a great company officer. It's not about being great at everything all at once. It's about being great at your current level and position.

84

**Be great at whatever level you are at.**
**Always seek feedback on areas to improve.**

*Courtesy: Div. Chief Johnny Winston, Jr. - FirefighterToolbox.com*

If you are in your first two years, for example, you can easily build a respected reputation within your group of peers, senior firefighters, and officers if you do the following:

▶ Do you have a "willingness to learn" attitude?

▶ Are you always looking to help?

▶ Are you the first one lined up to do the chores around the firehouse? Racking hose? Cleaning the equipment?

▶ Are you assisting the driver/operator with the engine checks?

▶ When you have free time in the firehouse, are you reading and studying?

▶ Are you learning the district?

▶ Are you asking others about the things you can study now to help you today with this crew? (And then do you do it?)

▶ Is your uniform in good repair and professional looking?

- Are you ready to go when the alarm goes off, or are you the last one on the apparatus?
- Are you cleaning up in the kitchen after meals? (Have you cleaned more dishes in your first year in the fire service than you did in all the years of your life combined before that?)
- Are you training/practicing your skills daily?
- Are you early to work and ready to go once you arrive?
- Are you taking notes and paying attention during company trainings?
- Are you the leader (eager to work) when it's time to rack hose and clean gear?
- Once you finish your cleaning assignment, do you go look to help others with theirs?
- Are you keeping yourself mentally sharp (no drugs, alcohol, sleep deprivation, etc.)?
- Are you keeping yourself physically fit?
- Are you looking to learn from others' experiences?
- Are you listening to the stories and experiences of others when in the firehouse?
- Are you asking questions in an effort to learn?
- Are you appreciating your officers and fellow firefighters by thanking them for sharing, teaching, and training with you?
- Are you buying a treat for your crew every so often as a sign of gratitude?
- Do you smile a lot and enjoy being a firefighter?

*If you are reading this book, you have likely answered "yes" to a lot of these questions. If you're reading this book, you most likely have a burning desire to be the best firefighter you can be.*

Let me ask you this question: If someone came on your shift and did all the above, would you respect them? Would you want them on your team? Would you want to help them succeed?

Building relationships is more about your attitude, your behavior, and your contributions than anything else, including your sex, race, background, or years on the job.

## GIVE A SMILE, GET A SMILE

When you are a new firefighter, you are always being evaluated, and if you are smiling all the time, it may alarm some people. New firefighters are to watch and learn perspective. They are not expected to come in and lead the conversations and set the tone for the shift by always smiling.

What I am referring to is this: If we want to be liked, we need to likable. If we want to be respected, we need to behave in a respectable fashion. It is part of human nature for people to judge others. Firefighters are judged on their behavior.

. . . . . . . . . . . . . . . . . . . . . . . . . . . . .

*Work so hard at your craft and on the job that others praise you. Let someone else praise you, but not yourself.*

— David J. Soler

. . . . . . . . . . . . . . . . . . . . . . . . . . . . .

Remember, great firefighters know and implement the following truism: "mouths closed, eyes open, ears listening, and work hard." Then they work, they work, and they work. This is why they are respected and this is what makes them great.

I can walk into any firehouse in this country and ask, "Who are the great firefighters? Who are the firefighters you respect here?" It will be obvious.

I guarantee you that their crewmates respect them and think they're great for what they have accomplished, what they continue to accomplish, how they make them feel, etc. These are all "doing" types of things. They are results of hard work and "doing work", not just talking about it.

. . . . . . . . . . . . . . . . . . . . . . . . . . . . . .

*Don't tell me what kind of firefighter you are.*
Just show me!

— David J. Soler

. . . . . . . . . . . . . . . . . . . . . . . . . . . . . .

I can also walk into any firehouse in this country and ask where the firefighter is who thinks they are God's gift to firefighting, and the group will be able to point to someone (if they're being honest). If I evaluate why they pointed to that person or what gave that person that reputation, it will often be because they brag about themselves. They tell everybody every little thing they do or did, and they give very little credit to anyone else. They usually have very strong jaw muscles because as the saying goes, "They're always running their mouth!"

Now, here is your decision: Which one are you? Are you a respected firefighter or God's gift to firefighting? Who do you want to be? What changes do you need to make?

# ACTION PLAN

▸ List the habits/behaviors you are going to implement and be committed to what respected firefighters do on a regular basis.

▸ Make a checklist and keep track of how often you complete your list (like a batting average in baseball).

# It's amazing how one extremely common denominator of great firefighters is humility.

— David J. Soler

STRATEGY #8

# GEAR UP DAILY WITH HUMILITY

# THERE IS NOTHING LESS ATTRACTIVE THAN AN ARROGANT FIREFIGHTER

I love being at a busy fire station that sees a lot of fire, because I get the opportunity to see through the facade of most ego-driven firefighters.

The fire will humble us and it can kill us. Unfortunately, for a lot of great firefighters, it has. Great firefighters respect the fire, its capabilities, and know that it can wreak havoc in a catastrophic way in just a glimpse of a moment.

**The firefighter cutting the hole in the roof is Eric J. Larson.
One of the most humble firefighters I know.**

The question is not *if*, but *when*. When you've spent enough time going to calls, you will have seen and dealt with some awful, awful stuff. As firefighters, we respect the fire because we are so often exposed to the devastation fire can do, both to property and people. We study the history of the fire service, stories of the great fires that took down cities, case studies of close calls and line-of-duty deaths (LODDs). Fires have broken the spirit of fire departments by killing our fellow brothers and sisters.

Where we go wrong is when we see our "bread-and-butter" (routine) calls over and over and become complacent. We become complacent when we go a long period of time without an injury or firefighter fatality. We err when we think that we are better equipped and better trained than the fire is.

## One of the greatest possible poisons that you see out there is arrogance.

— Battalion Chief Josh Fannon
Firefighter Toolbox Podcast, Episode 009

On average, about 100 firefighters die in the United States each year in the line of duty. (That is 1 brother or sister firefighter dying every 3.5 days, roughly.)

Most are from cardiac-related issues and driving incidents, but several are from the fire just being better than us. We can do everything right and still a firefighter dies. This happens every year.

Respected firefighters know this and therefore they stay humble. We understand the fact that we can do everything right and yet someone on our team will die. It is very tough to swallow when we go through this with someone we know and care about. These hurt the most because of the bond of brotherhood/sisterhood in the fire service. These LODDs are felt throughout the country and the fire service world.

. . . . . . . . . . . . . . . . . . . . . . . . . . . .

*Great firefighters stay aware of this fact.*
*They train as if their lives depended on it,*
*because they know it does.*

. . . . . . . . . . . . . . . . . . . . . . . . . . .

Great firefighters remember to always respect the devastation of the fire, no matter how many times or years we have conquered it. We remember that it only takes one time for it to devastate us, our department, and our community.

The other major turn-off with a big ego is that great firefighters know that it takes a team to be successful on the fire ground. No single firefighter can do it alone, no matter how great they are.

> Richard thought he was the world's greatest gift to firefighting. He was always ready to prove it with a story or example, such as how he opened a roof just in time or how he put out the devastating blaze.
>
> One day, Richard arrived at a working fire and got off the engine and grabbed the nozzle. He started to deploy the hose line and was going to make entry into the structure. He signaled to charge the line. He bled the line and made entry. He couldn't get far because there was a turn in the hallway. He was pulling and tugging. He was yelling to get more line as he wanted to move down the hall and up the stairs. He couldn't make the progress because he couldn't drag

the line all by himself. So he retreated as the fire kept moving at him. He saw the back-up nozzle firefighter and yelled, "What are you doing?!"

"I am watching your greatness!" retorted the back-up firefighter.

The moral of the story: Don't be a Richard!

There is very little we can do on the fire ground by ourselves. We rely on too many people to think that we "did it ourselves." Great firefighters know that even if they made the grab and rescued a person from the fire, they didn't do it themselves. From the radio dispatcher/communications monitor to the engine operator to the ventilation team to the fire extinguishment team to the incident commander, we need the team to be successful on the fire ground, and great firefighters never forget that. In those situations, respected firefighters are always looking to share the glory. They know that if it weren't for the others on the fire ground, they wouldn't be able to do their jobs.

# Humility is not a sign of weakness. It is a sign of strength.

— Capt Bryan T. Smith
Firefighter Toolbox Podcast, Episode 003

Great firefighters have a high personal standard and a very small ego. They know that it takes a team to be successful on the fire ground. The chain is only as strong as its weakest link, so they hold themselves to a high personal standard to be a strong link in the chain.

# ACTION PLAN

▶ Look for three people on every call that did something well and assisted on the call. Go and tell them, "Good job," and be specific about what they did so they know why you are patting them on the back.

▶ Look for acts of service around the fire station and thank the appropriate people. For example, thank the person who cleaned the dishes, who set up the training, who helped with dinner, etc.

▶ Look for ways to help those who are below you in rank and assist them in doing their job. Do things like helping them with the dishes, packing hose, or tasks that are the responsibilities of others. If you assist them in completing the work, it makes their workload easier.

STRATEGY #9

# BE A PURPOSE-DRIVEN FIREFIGHTER

# Being a firefighter and wearing the uniform is not about me. It's about something greater.

— Firefighter Preplan

## GREAT FIREFIGHTERS ARE PURPOSE-DRIVEN AND HAVE A PURPOSE GREATER THAN THEMSELVES.

*When you work, work as if you're working for something greater than just a paycheck. Work for your life's calling. Work for the Creator. Work for the greater good.*

*Great firefighters know they serve at the pleasure of the Big Chief, our Creator. No matter what our badges or uniforms say and no matter if we are paid or volunteer, we will always be accountable to the Big Chief whom I call* God *and some call the* Creator.

I know that not everyone in the fire service believes in the same God as I do. I also know that there are many different beliefs, including atheists, in the fire service.

To be transparent and forthright from my experience and interviews, I am sharing this in this book because this is a common denominator I have witnessed throughout my career and in interviews. If I left this out of the book, I would feel I was not being honest with the reader of this book, and it's not fair to those who have shared this as being a key to their success. My goal is to give the reader all that I know to be true.

The reader has the right to ignore this, endure this, or explore this for him or herself.

Throughout our careers, we will have to work with different officers and chiefs. Some will be great, some will not be great, and some may be awful. There may be times when we are in charge and make a decision that may not be ethical, and nobody will know. (Well, the Big Chief will know, and great and respected firefighters are aware of this.)

Great firefighters always do the ethical thing. They have integrity even when no one is looking. They know that treating people right and serving others is extremely important, and so that's what they do.

Their views of their jobs as firefighters include honor and privilege. They focus on the long-term view and the eternal rewards and consequences. Not everyone can be a firefighter because not everyone is trustworthy, selfless, or dedicated. God made some people that are willing to selflessly put themselves in harm's way. He made them willing to help others and personally sacrifice for others without reward. He called them *firefighters.*

Furthermore, great firefighters know that they are not God. They know that only God knows how life will unfold and only He understands the plan.

We as firefighters know that we are not God and cannot control life and death. We are just spokes in the wheel of life. We serve and we are on the front lines, but we definitely cannot control the outcome. We do our best and let God handle the rest.

> Not everyone can be a firefighter because not everyone is trustworthy, selfless, or dedicated. God made some people that are willing to selflessly put themselves in harm's way. He made them willing to help others and personally sacrifice for others without reward. He called them *firefighters.*
>
> —Firefighter Preplan

# Part of the overall fitness for a firefighter is the mental health part of the equation.

— Battalion Chief Patrick Kenny
  Firefighter Toolbox Podcast, Episode 013

When I just started out as a career firefighter, I was an EMT and driver for the medic unit. I had the opportunity to train with a paramedic named Nina, who had both great life and on-the-job experience. Throughout the different calls and shifts, I was always asking her questions and trying to learn as much as I could. She taught me a lot, but one thing stuck out the most.

Riding the medic unit on a busy department, we see lots of death. We had the exhilaration of being able to use our skills, tools, and teamwork to assist in preventing someone from dying—and we had others die right in our hands.

I remember asking her how she dealt with the death of her patients. This is what she told me.

"I don't take credit when they live, and so I don't take the credit or blame when they die."

I remember this like it was yesterday and I have adopted this belief as well, and it has helped me deal with the devastation that we see as emergency medical service (EMS) personnel, firefighters, and first responders.

Our job is to be the best we can be, to train hard, to know our skills to the best of our ability, to do the best we can, and to let God handle the rest.

Great firefighters know that they are not in control of who lives and who dies. We are not God. Only God can decide who lives and who dies. Great firefighters know that they work to be the best they can be and they put the rest in God's hands.

*I have been on calls and seen people survive a major wreck or a fire, and I've been on routine calls where the patient dies and leaves us scratching our heads. Consider the following story:*

A call came in around 2 am for a motor vehicle collision with entrapment/rescue. When we arrived, it was a mind-boggling call. This person was driving 50+ miles per hour and was, I believe, over the legal alcohol limit. There was a red light and at that red light was a U.S. mail tractor-trailer waiting. This person, for whatever reason, drove at 50+ mph directly into the back of the trailer of the truck. The car was crushed into the lower part of the trailer. The crossbar was inches from his head.

As we were extricating him, cutting the car, and trying to pull the car away from the back of the truck it had collided with, he was having a conversation with me and with others. I couldn't believe it. The car was so smashed that it was hard to even recognize that he was in a car. I couldn't even tell you what kind of car or truck it was. It was just red metal. It was an older auto because it was metal and not plastic or composites like cars are today.

The steering wheel was through the seat. He fortunately was to the side of it so it didn't crush his torso. His legs were somewhere in the crushed metal and we had called for the "go-team," which was a special unit from Johns Hopkins Hospital that would come to the scene to do an amputation.

It took a long time to figure out how to extricate him and actually get him extricated. We were all shocked that he was alive and even more amazed

102

that he was talking. We were able to extricate him without amputation and he lived. Amazing.

On another call, there was a motorcycle that collided with a compact car with a 22-year-old seat-belted male driver. The motorcycle had hit the turning car broad side and the car rolled over and the motorcycle driver was ejected from the motorcycle.

On arrival, both the motorcycle driver and the car driver were pronounced dead. The car driver was belted and had no major trauma to him except some blood from his ear. He seemed perfectly alright, but sat in the car, belted, and deceased.

I remember thinking, *Shouldn't we help him and do something. Isn't there something we can do?* The medic told me that because of the brain trauma and no pulse/no breathing, etc., it was a priority 4 according to protocols and the patient was pronounced dead.

(Disclaimer: I did not have extensive medical training at that time. There might have been more visual or known information that the medic had that I was unaware of.)

These were two different scenarios with two different outcomes. I remember this affecting me greatly and even having some feelings of guilt and asking questions like, *Could I have done more?* There are always so many "what-ifs."

Here is the thing: I am not God. I do not get to say when anyone's time is up. I can only train and be ready the best I can. I didn't take credit for when the person lived and so I don't get the blame when a person dies. It's all on God. I let God do the God work and I do the fire work that He has me do.

Great firefighters know that death and devastation are part of the job. You need to have the mindset to handle all the death and devastation and not just bury it emotionally or be emotionally numb to it. Because, if you do bury it, it plants a seed that eventually grows into negative emotions and leads to issues like post-traumatic stress disorder.

Respected firefighters know that it's admirable to reach out to others and qualified professionals for emotional help. Your department or your county may have these resources and, if not, there are a lot of national resources available. The key is to be prepared.

As firefighters, we know we will see death and devastation. How are you going to handle it? How do you process it? The answer to this question could mean your life, literally, because the stress from one call or the emotional toll from many calls can grab ahold of us emotionally and cause side effects. Some terms for this are *Critical Incident Stress Syndrome* and *Secondary Stress Syndrome*.

In order to have a long and rewarding career, you must understand that your emotions and emotional awareness are key skills and abilities that you must also learn. You must have a healthy mindset and resources available, such as people you can talk to, grieve with, and make sense of all this with. Learning how others have handled similar situations will bring great dividends for ourselves and others.

As of this writing, few if any firefighters get this type of training in school or at the academy, so there still is often a stigma around the fire service that having feelings is a sign of weakness. The truth is that we all have feelings— that's what makes us human. We don't want to lose that. We all need to be in relationships.

We all work hard to be able to make a difference and be ready when called upon. The truth is that it won't always work out the way we want it to. We, individually and as a fire service, are not perfect. We will make mistakes and people will die. Some of our own will die because of our mistakes. Those are very tough things to deal with.

Here's another thing: We can train to be the best, and people will still die. We can do everything right and our fellow firefighters or the people we have come to save will die. It has happened in the past and it will happen again, unfortunately. That is what makes this profession admirable—that despite all of these facts, we are still willing to go out there and do the job.

So, let's do the job emotionally. Let's learn how to process loss. Let's teach this at the kitchen table. Let's be strong enough and brave enough to admit that we all have feelings and emotions. Just like we need to clean our gear and remove the contaminants, we need to process emotions and clean out or heal from the emotional wounds that we encounter.

Bravery is not ignoring or burying those emotional wounds. Bravery is grieving and processing the emotions and wounds properly so that we can move forward in strength and wholeness.

Great firefighters and officers seek out resources, process their emotions properly, and encourage others to do so as well. They commend someone for seeking counsel. They allow them time to process the emotions of loss and devastation, and the meaninglessness we see on the fire ground and at emergency scenes.

Now, on the other hand, we can't be emotional basket cases on the emergency scene or fire ground. I am not saying that we need to be crying on the way to the hospital, but I am saying that there is a time for that and it needs to be done sooner rather than later.

I have seen some of the toughest firefighters I know be tested like this. I have more respect for them for getting the counseling and working through the emotions, loss, and grief. To me, seeking counseling is more brave than burying your emotions and pretending it didn't affect you—and then becoming depressed, hopeless or bitter.

Seeing this has also allowed me to learn how to deal with grief and loss myself. Seeing someone I admire as a firefighter and officer go through grief and loss but still get on the fire engine, now having even more purpose and more understanding that we are not God and are not in control, is admirable.

## RESOURCES FOR DEALING WITH GRIEF

Most members of the fire service wait until they truly think they're going to die, and for some of them it's too late. [Regarding mental stress and illness: Don't wait.]

— Battalion Chief Patrick Kenny
  Firefighter Toolbox Podcast, Episode 013

There are many resources that can help firefighters who are having issues in their emotional health and dealing with loss, post-traumatic stress, personal issues like divorce, loss of a family member, financial stress, etc.

(Disclaimer: The author and publisher are not affiliated with any of these organizations or resources in this chapter and are not endorsing or recommending them. The following is provided for informational purposes. It is recommended that you do your own research and due diligence on these resources and/or organizations.)

"Share the Load" offers a confidential 24/7 Fire/EMS helpline (**888-731-FIRE**). It is available to all firefighters and their families at no cost.

You will reach a fellow firefighter who has expertise on how to proceed with helping. It's really that simple. Call confidentially for yourself or to get advice on how to help someone else.

Be willing to call for yourself and demonstrate that it's okay to learn about these resources and use these emotional tools. Don't wait until it's too late! Be prepared. It won't take long in your fire service career to have to deal with emotional trauma.

## ADDITIONAL RESOURCES:

▸ *N.V.F.C Member Assistance Program (http://americanaddictioncenters. org/fire-services)*

▸ *Life Safety Initiative 13 (http://everyonegoeshome.com)*

▸ *Counseling Service for Fire Fighters (www.csff.info)*

▸ *Firefighter Behavioral Health Alliance (www.ffbha.org)*

▸ *Firefighters Support Foundation (www.ffsupport.org)*

▸ *Federation of Fire Chaplains (http://firechaplains.org)*

▸ *International Critical Incident Stress Foundation (http://icisf.org)*

▸ *National Fallen Firefighters Foundation (www.firehero.org)*

▸ *The Code Green Campaign (http://codegreencampaign.org)*

▸ *National Volunteer Fire Council (www.nvfc.org)*

▸ *Share the Load Program (http://www.nvfc.org/hot-topics/share-the-load-support-program-for-fire-and-ems)*

STRATEGY #10

# INVEST IN THE BROTHERHOOD/ SISTERHOOD

**Investing in the brotherhood leads to some of our best personal friendships.**

*Kristen & David Soler (left)*

*Brain & Lindsay Smoot (right)*

It isn't hard to find firefighters who have life-long friendships with their fellow firefighters, because we spend so much time with each other. We experience some really traumatic situations over and over, and sometimes the only ones who can relate are other firefighters.

Great firefighters know the importance of relationships and they invest in them. They are willing to be a friend on the fire ground, in the firehouse, and in personal lives.

How do firefighters get so many friends?

They are friends to those around them. They are quick to give a compliment or offer appreciation. They are there to lend a helping hand whether it is racking hose, studying for a test, or helping someone move.

Firefighters have a very good B.S. meter. (B.S. is a technical term in the fire service that means *bull shillacki*). We get to know people: what they can do, can't do, and what kind of person they truly are. Firefighters generally aren't afraid to call you out on it or even shun you out.

If people are not talking to you and you have been around awhile, it's usually a sign that you're not wanted, or they see through your B.S. Firefighters know this and they know that the best thing to do is to be honest, be humble, work hard, and be willing to help in all things as much as you can. If you do this, respect and friends will be plentiful.

I also wanted to share with you that most likely there will be someone who doesn't like you in the fire service. Great firefighters know that not everyone will like them and they are okay with it.

**Invest in your crew by building each other up.**

Courtesy: Div. Chief Johnny Winston, Jr. - FirefighterToolbox.com

They do know that if they follow the principles outlined in this book, someone may not *like* them, but they will still *respect* them. That other person will know that this firefighter can do the job.

Unfortunately, there are a lot of different personalities in the fire service. I would even venture to say that there is sexism, racism, lazy-ism. (This is when you hate someone just because they are lazy.)

You may find yourself in a situation where someone dislikes you for something you can't control like your race, background, sex, sexual orientation, etc. Or, they just don't like the fact that you are successful, or that others really like you, or maybe "you took their spot."

There are thousands of reasons why someone may not like you personally. Great firefighters know that they cannot control what other people think and that if they follow these principles, then enough of the good folks will like them and they will have a fun career around other great firefighters.

The other thing they know is that a lot of these so-called "haters" are probably just miserable in some way or hurting in some way deep down. They don't know how to deal with their emotions, their insecurities, or their wounds, so they may take it out on them in the form of bullying, teasing, manipulation, etc.

Remember that your reputation is built on what you do over time and not on just one incident or one person. People look at you as a whole. You may be in a miserable situation with a bad officer or someone who seems to be out to make your life miserable. Just know that if you keep following these principles, you will make it through it. Then, when others see how you perform, it will make the person who is trying to make your life miserable look bad themselves.

Another thing to consider is to get away from that situation. If you are at a career station and feel it is not a good fit and you are not getting a fair shake, transfer out. Do it as quickly as you can. There is no need to stay there and try to change the miserable, passive-aggressive people you're working with.

I also highly suggest that you evaluate the situation. Is there something you are not doing that you need to be doing? Are they riding you to improve your behavior? Are you being lazy in any way? Sometimes, the great crews will look for different ways to motivate you to correct a bad behavior. So, before you go thinking it's everybody else's fault, really evaluate if you are doing all the right things with the right attitude and in the right way.

It is also good to get feedback from someone you admire and trust, like a mentor, to help you evaluate if this situation is toxic enough for you to transfer or if you can use it for constructive improvement.

> Stay true to your values, despite being surrounded by negative personnel, situations, and culture
>
> — Walt Lewis
> Division Chief,
> Orlando Fire Department
> Listen to the "Brotherhood and Sisterhood in the Fire Service" podcast at:
> FirefighterToolbox.com/053

If you have sought out honest, non-biased advice about the situation, and you both feel that you *are* doing the right things and that this *is* a toxic situation, then move/transfer as soon as possible. Keep working hard and doing the right things and be patient for the transfer to come.

If you're a volunteer, a transfer may mean changing stations within the department or moving on to another department.

For major issues, I encourage you to go to the officers (and the officers above them) if the necessary and proper steps aren't taken to address the situation. Nonetheless, you can do all that and still not get anywhere because the officer on that shift or the culture of that volunteer firehouse is just that way, so transferring or moving on will be the best option.

I would say that one of the most common things I hear when I talk with chiefs, captains, firefighters, etc., in career departments is how they are so frustrated with the culture and poor leadership. They speak about how the accountability and fairness is minimal or nonexistent. I personally have been in some very challenging situations, and that's not unique to me.

I share this with you because, just like on the fire ground where you can do everything right and still get killed. In the fire station, you can do everything right and still not be wanted. Don't take it personally (and I know that's easy to say and hard to do). The fact that they wouldn't want a person who follows these principles is more of a negative reflection on them than it is on you.

They may talk bad about you and even make up lies about you. They will try to put you in positions to fail. They may even set you up on purpose to fail. This is an effort to pull people to their way of thinking—or to really make you miserable. It hurts. Believe me, I know. But know that this will pass. Your reputation is not just with them; it's over the whole body of work.

Keep doing the right things, and look to get to a station with other great and respected firefighters and officers. Work hard, follow these principles, and you will succeed! Just remember that it takes time. It's about consistent behavior, over and over during a long period of time.

# ACTION PLAN

1. Review this chapter as needed.

2. Make a list of ways you can appreciate others in the fire service.

3. Identify 3 people who you appreciate. Write them a personal note or email thanking them for something specific that they do or did that you appreciate.

# It's not about you. It's about the people that you're serving and the community, but even more so, it's about the people who are working with you.

—Division Chief Johnny Winston Jr.
Firefighter Toolbox Podcast,
Episode 041

STRATEGY #11

# BE PREPARED FOR THE UNCONTROLLED AND CONTROLLED CHAOS OF THE FIRE SERVICE

## WHO'S IN CONTROL AND
## WHY DO THESE THINGS HAPPEN?

In the fire service, we are the ones called upon for emergencies. This is a gift, a privilege, and a challenge. We will see ultimate destruction as in 9/11, Hurricane Katrina, and many other events. We will see tremendous sadness when going on EMS calls or patient assist calls when people are at their lowest points in life with few to no family or friends who care about them—so much so that they die from neglect.

Be prepared for the uncontrolled and controlled chaos
of the fire service: both in the station and on the fire ground.

*Courtesy: Capt. Bryan T. Smith - FirefighterToolbox.com*

## What to expect as a firefighter:

We will be:  Under-appreciated
Under-paid (if at all)
Over-worked
Over-stressed (everything we do could mean life or death)
Asked to do more and more with less and less

In addition to fires, we will be the answer to all of our communities'
problems, such as:
Water in their basement
A tree that fell on their house
Being stuck in an elevator
Spilling hazardous chemicals
Locking their keys in their car with their child in it
Falling down a ravine on a 4-wheeler

We will go from responding to life and death calls to performing mundane
activities, such as:
Cleaning and washing our gear and equipment
Cleaning our stations
Cooking
Repairing our equipment
Maintaining our equipment

In summary, know that when in doubt, the dispatcher mostly dispatches
the fire service.

# THE CAREER-LONG HEAD-SCRATCHING QUESTIONS THAT ARE DEBATED AT FIRE STATION KITCHEN TABLES ACROSS THE COUNTRY ARE:

- Why do we always do what we always have done?
- Why don't we change as a fire service?
- Why do people do such stupid things?
- Why do they just expect us to know everything and solve everything?
- Why is there so much death and destruction in this world?
- Why is there so much pain and hurt?

## CAN I CONTROL IT? WHAT CAN I CONTROL?

Great firefighters know that there are some things they can control and some things they cannot. They know that they can control their attitude, their behavior, and their actions. They know that change starts with them and that if they want to see something change, they can start by seeing themselves do it first.

They lead by example and know that some things and some people just don't make sense. Nonetheless, they focus and work on the things they can control and let God handle the rest.

Great firefighters think on and ask for guidance through the serenity prayer.

**Serenity Prayer** by Reinhold Niebuhr (Long Version)

*God, give me grace to accept with serenity*
*the things that cannot be changed,*
*Courage to change the things*
*which should be changed,*

120

*and the Wisdom to distinguish*
*the one from the other.*
*Living one day at a time,*
*Enjoying one moment at a time,*
*Accepting hardship as a pathway to peace,*
*Taking, as Jesus did,*
*This sinful world as it is,*
*Not as I would have it,*
*Trusting that You will make all things right,*
*If I surrender to Your will,*
*So that I may be reasonably happy in this life,*
*And supremely happy with You forever in the next.*
*Amen.*

Here is the shortened version for ease of memory:

**Serenity Prayer** by Reinhold Niebuhr

*God, grant me the serenity to accept the things I cannot change,*
*The courage to change the things I can,*
*And the wisdom to know the difference.*

Ultimately, we are not in control of a lot things, and we spend our time trying to control the things we cannot instead of the things we can. Understand the difference, focusing on what you can change, and then acting on it. Then let God handle the rest.

# ACTION PLAN

1. Focus on what you can change and do it.

2. Refer to the Serenity Prayer as needed

STRATEGY #12

**BE READY TO WEATHER
THE CAREER AND LIFE STORMS**

There will be storms. Plan for them. Expect them. Then don't just survive it, thrive through it!

We all go through the storms of life and if we are in the fire service for any significant amount of time, we will have career storms.

Career storms come in many different forms, ranging from having weak officers who are not doing their job to major injuries.

Some storms to be aware of:

- Poor leadership
- Being in a station or crew that is not a good fit
- Injuries
- Death of a fellow firefighter
- Being passed over for a promotion
- Mental stress
- Having to work with others who are not looking out for you and who are providing mental anguish
- Being treated unfairly
- Being sued
- Being suspended or written up justly or unjustly
- Making a major mistake
- Being lied to
- Crazy rule changes
- Changes due to politics that seem to hurt the fire department
- Being discriminated against
- Being the subject of harassment
- Line-of-duty death
- Off-duty death
- Political/administrative changes that affect you personally

As much as I want the fire service to be perfect and to be the perfect example of brotherhood/sisterhood, the truth is that the fire service is imperfect and is run by imperfect people. Nobody is perfect, including us.

Therefore, let this be your notice that no fire department is perfect. No firefighter job or position is perfect, and you will have challenges. We don't know when or where the challenges will be or for how long, but we know they exist and that they will come and strike our careers.

Here is what successful firefighters do: they learn from the examples of others who have had these storms, study how they handled it, and get through the storm with a positive outcome.

**Pre-planning is important.**

1. Be aware that these career/life storms exist,
2. Learn from the examples of others who have had these storms and studied how they handled it and
3. Learn/Observe how others got through the storm with a positive outcome.
4. Search for other resources to assist you.

Just like we prepare for a real storm in the fire service, you will need to prepare for a storm in your career. Here are some ways to do this:

FIREFIGHTER PREPLAN

# 1. HAVE A MENTOR OR ADVISOR

Have someone you can trust who is not in your fire station. This should be someone who is not personally connected to the situation but understands the situation and its politics. They should be someone you can talk with about what has happened and get advice from for resolving or mitigating the situation.

It's important to have someone not connected to the situation. A substantial amount of firefighters have their Captain or officer as their mentor. Although it's great to have your captain as a mentor, when a "career storm" comes (i.e. - your captain does something ill-advised and you get the blame): who are you to talk with?

Your mentor would be a great resource. However, in these cases, your officer or "boss" is at the center of the issue with you. It seems you will have a conflict of interest confiding in your mentor who is also your boss. In one quick instance, you would have lost respect for your boss and lost your mentor all at the same time.

It can be nice to have your captain as your mentor, but also consider additional mentors and advisors for situations like these.

> We can do everything right and still have something bad happen to us. So we've got to constantly be on the watch.
>
> — Battalion Chief Brian Kazmierzak
> Firefighter Toolbox Podcast, Episode 006

## 2. HAVE A TRUSTED SUPPORT GROUP

Many of us are familiar with the following fire service saying:

"Telegraph, telephone, tell-a-firefighter."

In essence, the fastest way for information to get spread around, and usually misinterpreted or misconstrued, is to tell a firefighter. We are so used to talking with each other and "passing on information," that we have mastered the art of "pass-on."

Now with texting and social media (such as Facebook and Twitter), firefighters are even more lethal at spreading information.

Although we in the fire service use texting and social media for many beneficial reasons, it unfortunately is used for many hurtful ways like spreading gossip and rumors. When you make a mistake, realize that you probably will not want people knowing about the situation, especially the details of the situation. But, it *will* get talked about and spread around like skunk spray.

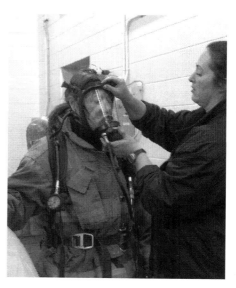

"Like Iron Sharpens Iron, One Firefighter Sharpens Another."
-Proverbs 27:17 (paraphrased)

Courtesy: Shauna Baccus

The solution is to have a trusted support group. You need one to three friends you can talk with confidentially—people who care about you and will keep the situation and information confidential, but will allow you to share your frustrations, pains and fears with them. They can provide you with perspective on the situation and encourage you through it.

This is easier said than done. These are people you would have to be willing to do the same thing for. This is something that takes time to build, because trust is built over time.

The key is to start building the support group before the storm happens. Have you ever tried to buy water or milk or bread right before a storm? It's gone. Usually there is nothing left. But a simple plan of buying and stocking up on these items when there is no storm is very easy to do.

So look to build a confidential support group where all of you agree to be confidential with each other and help each other through the storms. These individuals will most likely end up being great, life-long friends. Unfortunately, some may still break that trust. So preplan for that, too!

## 3. HAVE OUTSIDE RESOURCES AND SUPPORT

Sometimes we get so entrenched with our career that it becomes our life. Firefighting may just be our job, but then we end up befriending our fellow firefighters and officers, so it becomes our social life as well. Then we date or marry someone in the fire service and it becomes our family life, too.

It's important to have outside resources, especially when a career storm comes. Being able to break away or have a boundary from the fire service will be crucial to thriving through the storm.

When these storms come, we will need to find "safe shelter." This metaphorical safe shelter should come from someplace other than the fire service. We need someplace we can go to get away from those who have a knowledge of the inner workings or what is happening on the job, shift or in the union.

It will feel like everyone is watching you and you don't know whom to trust. So having some non-fire service friends and resources will feel much safer for understanding what is happening and deciding how to deal with the situation. Since these people or resources have no direct or indirect connection with the fire service (as far as your career or your fire department politics go), they have no career benefit in breaking confidentiality.

## 4. SPIRITUAL RESOURCE

*I know that everyone reading this book may not believe in the same God as I do—or they may not believe in a god at all. But, to be fully transparent, I want to share what has worked for me and others.*

During these times, I (and many others I have gotten close with and interviewed) have shared that we can lean on God for love, especially if we were being falsely persecuted. This gives us a sense of knowing that it will all work out—this storm will soon pass.

So I encourage you to seek God for strength and encouragement during these times.

# ACTION PLAN

▶ Get a mentor and advisor (multiple mentors and advisors if possible).

▶ Start building a trusted support group.

▶ Start building outside the fire service resources and support groups.

▶ Start building spiritual resources and a relationship with God.

STRATEGY #13

**KEEP FOCUSED AND
STAY MOTIVATED**

# Firefighters: Train like your life depends on it, because it does.

—Anonymous
(But a wise firefighter)

# HOW DO WE KEEP FOCUSED AND STAY MOTIVATED?

## *W.I.N.*

W.I.N. stands for "What's Important Now?"

In each stage of our careers and on each shift or call, there are certain things that are always the most important to do. Those are the things that you must do. If you ask yourself, "What's important now?" and answer it honestly, you can guide yourself to greatness by doing what's important now. If you ask yourself and honestly don't know what's important now—things you should do or learn—then you need to seek out a mentor. You need someone who is further down the path than you are and you need to get their input. The key is to continually make positive steps. Small steps are great and big steps are fortunate when they come, but the key is movement.

Don't get overwhelmed. Know that you cannot do everything all at once. Being a great and respected firefighter is a process and journey. It's about doing little things over and over with consistency.

I learned the W.I.N. acronym from Lou Holtz, former football head coach of Notre Dame, and I adapted it to my fire service career.

If your job is to be at your shift at 7 AM, ask yourself, "What's important now?" Answer: It's being at your shift early and ready to go—that is "what's important now."

You get to the firehouse and ask yourself, what's important now? Getting your gear ready, getting your pass-on information, checking your SCBA and radio, and reviewing the engine or truck you are riding—so do these things.

**E815, E814, T831 crews doing work.**

*Courtesy: Author, JMVFC.org and the city of Edgewood.*

You're on your shift and you have free time, ask yourself what's important now? Studying my book? Reading some articles? Reviewing the engine? Exercising? The answer to the question is usually pretty clear once you ask yourself. Decide on "what's important now" and get to work on it. Don't worry about anything else. When it's time to go home, what's important now? You'll probably want to give the "pass-on," get cleaned up, and go be with your family.

This simple question will lead you to continually take small steps that lead to accomplishing your tasks and staying focused and on mission without getting overwhelmed. The discipline of this behavior will garner you respect and admiration from your peers and officers.

# ACTION PLAN

1. Get an index card and write on it:

   "W.I.N." (What's Important Now?)

2. Keep the index card in your pocket. Every time you check your pocket for your phone, keys, wallet, it will remind you to ask yourself that question. Then act on it.

   (The index card will wear out and eventually get destroyed. This gives you the opportunity to re-write the card, which further solidifies the thought process in your mind. You can add this saying as a wallpaper screen on your phone.)

# Training is the foundation upon which all good firefighters are built.

—Bryan T. Smith
Captain,
Baltimore County Fire Dept.
Firefighter Toolbox

STRATEGY #14

# USE THE FIREFIGHTER TRAINING
# SUCCESS DIAMOND

# If you're failing to train, you're training to fail.

—David J. Soler

## FIREFIGHTER MASTERY

**Step 1:** Certification Training
**Step 2:** Hands-On Training
**Step 3:** Live/Real Fire Ground Experience
**Step 4:** Enhancement Training

After many years of trying to master the art and science of firefighting and studying the patterns of what makes a great firefighter on the fire ground, the Firefighter Training Success Diamond (FTSD) was born as a model to emulate.

Like in baseball, the object is starting at home plate. Then go to first base safely, then to second base safely, then to third base, and finally back home. This doesn't win you the game, but it scores points for you.

## STEP 1: CERTIFICATION TRAINING
### (FROM HOME TO 1ST BASE)

The FTSD should be viewed in such a way. Starting at home (the bottom of the diamond), the way you get to first base is to take a certification or foundational type of training in a particular subject area. So if we are talking basic firefighting, then taking Firefighter I & II, or the equivalent of your academy training, gets you to first base.

. . . . . . . . . . . . . . . . . . . . . . . . . . . . . .

*A firefighter without training is
like an unsharpened pencil: Pointless.*

— Firefighter Toolbox

. . . . . . . . . . . . . . . . . . . . . . . . . . . . . .

## STEP 2: HANDS-ON TRAINING
### (FROM 1ST BASE TO 2ND BASE)

To go from first base to second base, you need to become proficient for that expertise. We call this hands-on training or proficiency. So in this example of basic firefighting, if you have taken the class and passed it, that's step one. Step two is taking that knowledge, skills, and abilities to become proficient on the fire ground. You must be able do this confidently and on your own. This is hands-on training.

## STEP 3: LIVE/REAL FIRE GROUND EXPERIENCE
### (FROM 2ND BASE TO 3RD BASE)

. . . . . . . . . . . . . . . . . . . . . . . . . . . .

*The more you train, the easier it gets.*

— David J. Soler

. . . . . . . . . . . . . . . . . . . . . . . . . . . .

The next level is to gain experience using that knowledge, skills, and abilities on the fire ground—not just a few times, but many, many times. It can take months or years depending on the area of expertise and the call volume. Some firefighters never master this level because they don't get the type of calls needed to perform the skills and abilities. This is called getting live/real fire ground experience.

## STEP 4: ENHANCEMENT TRAINING
### (FROM 3RD BASE TO HOME)

. . . . . . . . . . . . . . . . . . . . . . . . . . .

*Only train on the skills you*
*want to keep. Forget the rest.*

— David J Soler

. . . . . . . . . . . . . . . . . . . . . . . . . . .

The next level is enhancement training. You are enhancing your experience, knowledge, skills, and abilities in the subject area by learning from other subject matter experts, whether they are in your department, outside your department, on a national level, or on an international level.

This includes studying and learning national "best practices" from the subject matter experts for the particular subject. This is where going to national training conferences, reading blogs, and watching videos from subject matter experts fits in. Continuing education on a subject or refresher training on the "latest and greatest" of this subject would fit into this category as well.

The key here is not to just read it or hear it, but to actually implement it into your skill set and knowledge base so you are continually enhancing your knowledge, skills, and abilities on this subject.

We call this *firefighter enhancement training*. (Bryan T. Smith coined this term.)

Once you "round the bases," you will be in the mastery level for that particular skill or ability.

As a firefighter, you may round the bases for firefighter training, but then you may look to become a driver/operator. So, you start at home again and take the certification/college/foundational classes to become a driver. Then you train to become proficient on the *training* fire ground and on the road. Then you will need to perform and become proficient on the *live* fire ground. Then you need to gain experience with all scenarios in live situations. Then you will train for enhancement.

No matter which area the firefighter wants to learn or develop their knowledge, skills, and abilities, this is the map to follow to mastery.

Here are some examples of the different areas of mastery for firefighters:

- Firefighter
- Driver/Pump Operator
- Driver/Ladder Operator
- Engine Firefighter
- Truck Firefighter
- Emergency Medical Technician
- Hazardous Materials Technician
- Hazardous Materials Operator
- Hazardous Materials Specialist
- Rescue Technician (Vehicle, Swift-Water, Dive, etc.)
- High Angle Rescue Technician
- Ship Board Firefighter
- Fire Boat Operator
- R.I.T./R.I.C./F.A.S.T Firefighter Crew
- Line Officer
- Lieutenant
- Captain
- Incident Commander
- Safety Officer
- E.M.S.

These are just some of the advanced training or specialty training options that firefighters will have the opportunity to pursue during their careers. With the ever-evolving skill of firefighting and more demands put on the fire service, this list is just a sample and is ever growing. But each specialty has us start at home plate on the Firefighter Success Diamond for our opportunity to master that level.

This understanding and visual aid provides you with the proper sequence and depth for mastery of the many skills and abilities found in a fire service career.

# ACTION PLAN

1. Identify and make a list of the skills/areas you would like to master.

2. Identify where you are "on the bases" with those skills/areas.

3. Plan out your next steps for getting to the next base.

4. Take action!

# There are days when we do not feel like training, but great firefighters do it anyway. Train hard. Stay safe.

—David J. Soler
Firefighter Toolbox

STRATEGY #15

# HAVE A FIREFIGHTER-STRONG HEALTH PROGRAM

........................................

*Can't do much as a firefighter*
*if you're weak, sick, or out of shape.*

—Firefighter Toolbox

........................................

Great firefighters know that health and strength play a vital role in being successful as a firefighter. They treat it seriously and continue to learn in this area as well as build great habits.

As firefighters, we put our bodies through tremendous amounts of stress, both physically and emotionally: from sleep deprivation, caffeine overloads, to racing heart rates and adrenaline rushes on the fire ground.

The thing that great firefighters do is to maintain a strong foundation of health and fitness. I will share with you in a moment about the foundation that great firefighters build, but unfortunately there are some things that we do as firefighters that are just part of the territory.

For example, sleep deprivation is one of the worst things you can do to your body and your health. There is a tremendous number of studies (Google them) that document that we need proper amounts of sleep (from 6-8 hours) at the same time/routine each day.

Unfortunately, as paid firefighters, this is something that we have to compensate for because we are expected and paid to go out on calls all through the night. Even if we volunteer, all the good calls and fires are usually at night. This is something that I have not found a magic wand to eliminate. If we have a strong health and fitness foundation, however, we can handle the disturbances better than if we don't.

In this chapter, I am providing a valuable overview because, in essence, it would take a whole other book to explain everything and go into detail on this.

Nonetheless, here is a brief overview.

Great firefighters have become firefighter strong by building a healthy foundation in these four pillars of health and fitness:

**Pillar 1**- Strength Training
**Pillar 2**- Cardiovascular Training
**Pillar 3**- Nutrition and Hydration
**Pillar 4**- Flexibility

All four pillars are required for being *firefighter strong*. When someone lacks in one or more areas, they become less effective and even unproductive on the fire ground. Some have even become a liability on the fire ground due to a lacking health and fitness foundation.

## STRENGTH TRAINING PROGRAM

Strength training is to build strength. This allows us to pick things up that are heavy, throw ladders, and carry people. Firefighters need strength because the tools, equipment, and tasks are heavier and require more strength than is usually needed in non-firefighting activities. For example, a painter's ladder is not as heavy as the same size firefighting ladder. Firefighter tools and equipment have to be stronger and handle more abuse then their non-firefighting counterparts.

In addition, we wear our turnout gear and SCBA while working on the fire ground, so this adds another dimension and need for strength and fitness to perform on the job.

If you are not strong enough to pick up, move, and set up the tools and equipment, then you will not be very effective on the fire ground.

This area tends to be the weaker area for women firefighters due to their natural physical make-up as compared to men. Nonetheless, this is not a limiting factor for women. Many great firefighters who are women, know the importance of a weight-training program and are on one. Because they have built and maintained their strength, they perform very well on the fire ground and are valuable assets to the team.

Furthermore, there are many male firefighters who are not on a strength-training program. Consequently, they have become weak physically and cannot perform well on the fire ground. They are ineffective and require extra help with doing certain assignments because of their physical shortcomings.

Great firefighters know that it is important to be on a strength-training program throughout their careers to ensure they can perform on the fire ground. They know that it does not matter if we are male or female; both can be strong and effective. They also know that some firefighters of both sexes have become complacent, physically weak, and cannot perform on the fire ground.

Great firefighters have a strength-training program that they continue to follow throughout their careers.

## CARDIOVASCULAR PROGRAM

A cardiovascular program helps to build and maintain our aerobic capacity. If strength training determines how much we can lift or how strong we are, then our cardio health determines how long we can do it.

This is probably not the first time you have heard this, as there is a tremendous number of studies and reports on this topic and lots of articles and resources at FirefighterToolbox.com.

Let me share how this affects you on the fire ground:

On the fire ground, we need to be able to "go the distance." We need to be able to do multiple tasks throughout the incident and then clean up and put everything away and get ready for the next call.

Having a great cardiovascular program will give us great cardiovascular health. This will allow us to conserve more air and not have to change our SCBA cylinder as often.

Studies have shown that having good cardiovascular health also decreases our risk of heart disease and other health ailments. Since the number one cause of LODDs (line of duty deaths) in the fire service is cardiac events, we need to pay close attention to and ensure we have a good cardiovascular program throughout our careers and beyond.

Cardiovascular exercise includes activities like running, biking, swimming, aerobics, etc. The key is that we are doing an activity that raises our heart rate above a certain percentage but not so high that it puts too much stress on our heart.

Here is a definition from Wikipedia (Courtesy - http://en.wikipedia.org/wiki/Aerobic_exercise):

*Aerobic exercise (also known as **cardio**) is physical exercise of low to high intensity that depends primarily on the aerobic energy-generating process. Aerobic literally means "relating to, involving, or requiring free oxygen," and it refers to the use of oxygen to adequately meet energy demands during exercise via aerobic metabolism. Generally, light-to-moderate intensity activities that are sufficiently supported by aerobic metabolism can be performed for extended periods of time.*

## FIREFIGHTER PREPLAN TIP

Decide on what type of activity you will do for your cardio program.

Schedule it into your calendar and make it automatic, just like an appointment.

Find a training buddy to exercise with or just to meet them at the same location for accountability and encouragement.

## NUTRITION AND HYDRATION

This area is one that may require that you read books that can explain it, but I will do my best to give an overview and provide some understanding.

If you have a champion race horse that is worth millions of dollars and you wanted that race horse to be able to live long and perform well, what would you feed it?

Let me ask it another way: If you had a champion firefighter that does a priceless job and you need that champion firefighter to be healthy and strong and ready to perform so lives can be saved, what would you feed him/her?

Hopefully, you would say you would feed them the most nutritious foods that meet all their nutrition needs.

Unfortunately, as you hang out at fire stations all over the country, you will see these champion thoroughbreds eating the least nutritional food at the worst times and drinking toxic chemical-laden drinks.

However, there are firefighters who understand proper and healthy nutrition and most likely there are some in your fire station or fire department. If you study them, you will find that they have more energy, look better, and get sick less frequently than the others. You will find them performing on the fire ground better and longer.

This chapter is not to give you a specific plan or to debate how much of what food is ideal or how often you need to eat. It is here to make you aware that you are a champion thoroughbred firefighter who has thousands and thousands of dollars invested in training, gear, pay, equipment, etc. Therefore, be cognizant of what you are feeding that champion.

Do more research on what is healthy and what is not. Develop a meal plan for maximal health and energy. It will give you great dividends in your fire service career and on the fire ground.

In addition, hydration is extremely important. Making sure we are properly hydrated on a regular basis will yield great rewards. Again, there are a lot of studies on this and we have articles about hydration at FirefighterToolbox. com.

Know that we need certain amounts of water on a day-to-day basis. As our exercise increases, we need additional water, and in weather conditions that are very hot, we will need additional hydration.

When I compete in triathlons, poor hydration affects my performance. While competing, I have to know how much water to drink on a regular basis to always stay hydrated. My hydration levels of the days and weeks leading up to the event had a direct effect on my performance the day of the triathlon. I discovered through researching, learning from other athletes, and then testing it for myself a formula for a baseline hydration.

The starting point is 1/2 ounce of water per pound of body weight per day. So if you weigh 180 pounds, you will need at least 90 ounces of water per day for proper hydration. If you are involved in exercising or dealing with weather conditions like high heat, you need additional hydration and possibly electrolytes.

Another visual test is by looking at your urine. If you are properly hydrated, your urine will be clear. Keep drinking water until your urine is a very faint yellow or clear.

Some people have learned falsely that we are dehydrated only when we are thirsty. If you are thirsty, you are already dehydrated, so don't use that as a "signal" of when to drink water.

One of the best ways to always know our hydration level is to monitor our urine color. Our properly hydrated urine color is clear to slightly yellow tint. Anything darker than that would mean dehydration (e.g. - The darker the yellow color the more dehydrated we are). Other colors in our urine represent other health issues that we must seek medical advice for.

## FLEXIBILITY

**When it comes to the job of firefighting, the scientific research tells us that you actually need to possess all the components of fitness.**

—Dr. Karlie Moore
Firefighter Toolbox Podcast, Episode 017

For most of my life I did not take stretching very seriously. This is coming from a college athlete and triathlete. I did stretch, but I did not learn all of its foundational principals and how to properly do it.

I just did as I was taught in sports and from others. As I am now older and have gone through some serious injuries, I wish I knew then what I know now. It would have saved myself a lot of mental anguish and down time.

Flexibility is very important and it prevents injuries. Having flexibility gives us energy and allows us to deal with unexpected events. Let me explain.

On a smells-and-bells call, we were walking through the building and I came upon a wet spot that was hard to see. I stepped like normal not knowing it was wet and slippery. I ended up sliding into a lunge-type split. I was flexible at the time and I was not injured.

However, my ego was bruised as everyone got to laugh at me during the call (and beyond) as they kept asking if I was doing figure skating on my time off. But it was all good firefighter fun.

Now, if I hadn't been flexible, I most likely would have injured myself. Another issue with not being flexible is that it limits what we can do on the fire ground, such as searching and crawling around, climbing ladders, stretching hose, etc.

Most times, people around you might not notice, but you will know if you are not able to do what you once did. As we get older, this is much more obvious. Now, you don't have to be as flexible as a gymnast, but let's make sure you're not a walking halligan bar either.

Let this serve as awareness and encouragement that stretching and having flexibility is important for a healthy firefighter career and for the prevention of injuries.

Look to incorporate stretching into your exercise program and remember that it is valuable.

## FIREFIGHTER PREPLAN TIP

Having a health program is extremely important for a successful fire service career. View yourself as a champion thoroughbred firefighter.

# ACTION PLAN

▶ Design a *firefighter-strong* health program that covers all four areas, including your hydration. Check out other books and resources for designing a specific health program for yourself.

▶ Schedule your workouts. Make it an appointment just like your job is.

▶ Look to get a workout buddy or two. Identify a few possible candidates and ask them if they are interested. Adding the social aspect keeps us more accountable and it makes it more fun for most of us.

▶ Read some health and fitness articles on Firefighter Toolbox.

STRATEGY #16

**HAVE A CAREER PLAN**

# If you're failing to plan, then you're planning to fail.

—Benjamin Franklin

A career plan is simply a written down set of goals that you would like to achieve in your fire service career. It can also be a very detailed step-by-step plan—something that can change as you change throughout your career.

Having a vision for what you would like to accomplish in your career is important for you to achieve the rewarding career you seek. No chief I have ever met or interviewed just stumbled on being chief. They decided beforehand that they would like to have that opportunity and then they worked towards it.

Sometimes, the path to become chief or any other position in the fire service happens unorthodoxly, but they just didn't wake up one day as chief or pump operator or any other position.

What would you like to do in your fire service career? What positions would you like to fulfill? What trainings or certifications would you like to complete? What skills would you like to master? When would you like to do this?

Answering these questions is the start of your career plan.

## WHY IS IT IMPORTANT TO HAVE A CAREER PLAN?

Like I stated earlier, a great fire service career will not fall in your lap; you will have to think about and decide on what kind of positions you would like to have in your career. Do some research on the qualifications and certifications needed for these positions as well as the testing and approval/hiring process for positions, such as captain or chief.

Mostly, everyone who has gone through their career *with* a plan achieves most if not all of their goals. The plan is a guideline or map. It allows us to start the thinking process of what we need to do and who we need to become in order to get to where we want to go.

If we don't know where we want to go, we will be lost. You can't hit what you're not aiming for. Every fire we go to, we have a plan. We just don't show up and see what happens. Most likely the plan is to save lives and property and extinguish the fire and/or mitigate the emergency.

## FIREFIGHTER PREPLAN TIP

Have a career plan. Start thinking about the plan for your career.

**We may not know where we end up,
but we know where we can start. Start right where you are.**

*Courtesy: Engine Company 2, Ridgefield Park Fire Dept.*

# ACTION PLAN

1. Brainstorm all the things you would like to achieve in your career. Ask yourself questions, such as the following:

   - What is the plan for your career?
   - What positions do you want to obtain?
   - What trainings/certifications do you want to obtain?
   - What do you want to specialize in?
   - What units/stations do you want to work at?
   - What officers/crews would you like to work with?
   - Other...

2. Place a timeframe next to that item (e.g. 1–3 years, 3–5 years, 5+ years).

3. Start researching your 1–3 year goals to know what you need to do to qualify.

4. Start working on those items.

# Like iron sharpens iron, so one firefighter sharpens another.

—Proverbs 27:17
(paraphrased)

STRATEGY #17

# HAVE A MENTOR
# AND BE A MENTOR

It is critically important to have a mentor and to be a mentor. Firefighters who have a rewarding career have mentors and become mentors to others.

## WHAT IS A MENTOR?

A mentor is someone you respect and would like to emulate—someone who has some experience and wisdom in the fire service greater than or in addition to yours and is willing to give trusted and wise advice.

A mentor could be someone you may talk to daily or they might be someone you only talk to once every few months. It could be someone you only know through books and audio like a podcast. It's ultimately someone you look to for advice and guidance.

Having multiple mentors is very common.

## WHAT IS THE DIFFERENCE BETWEEN AN OFFICER AND A MENTOR?

An officer is a position in the fire service. They are in essence the boss for that crew/station/shift/department. They generally teach and guide in addition to lead, but they will not always be able to give you the words you want or need to hear.

An officer can be a mentor. If your officer is your mentor also, they would have to fulfill the officer role first before the mentor role. This is the weakness of having your only mentor as your officer as well.

Thanks for your mentorship Bryan T. Smith!

# Find yourself a mentor. Find people who are doing things right and emulate them.

— Deputy Chief Frank Viscuso
Author Step Up & Lead
FirefighterToolbox Podcast, Episode 002

## WHY IS IT IMPORTANT TO HAVE A MENTOR?

It's important to have a mentor for multiple reasons. You need:

▶ Someone to garner advice from
▶ Someone to study how they perform tasks
▶ Someone you trust who can give perspective on certain situations or circumstances

165

▶   Someone to act as a guide

## WHY BE A MENTOR?

▶   It's extremely rewarding to serve others and to pour knowledge into their lives. We can make a lasting impact on someone else by being a trusted mentor.

▶   We get to "pass on" our learned wisdom and experiences, which gives our work longer life and allows us to be a part of something bigger than ourselves.

▶   We get to serve others. It doesn't matter if we have one year or twenty years in the fire service; we can always be a mentor to someone who is behind us on the trail. Furthermore, we get to see others succeed.

▶   It's a great reminder that what we are doing is being watched. Sometimes, we think that what we do doesn't matter. When we mentor others, it reminds us that we are setting an example, letting our actions be the positive example that others should emulate.

## HOW DO YOU GET A MENTOR?

▶   One source of mentorship is reading books like this and listening to podcasts/audio programs (such as those found at FirefighterToolbox. com). For many years, I was mentored by people who didn't know me, but I knew them through their books and audio programs.

▶   Look inside and outside your department for people you respect and would like to emulate. In other words, ask yourself, "Would I like to trade places with that person?" If yes, you've found a starting point for pursuing a mentor.

You can simply get to know them and ask if they would be willing to share some career advice with you. Ask them if they would answer some questions you may have regarding your fire service career from time to time.

Generally, asking someone to be a mentor is not the way to go about it. Asking them questions and taking them to lunch is a more realistic approach. There is no set way of how to do it. It is about developing a relationship with them and letting them "pour into you". Some will respond positively to it and make themselves available and some will not, for whatever reason.

**Mentorship is the best gift in the fire service.**

*Courtesy: Div. Chief Johnny Winston, Jr. - FirefighterToolbox.com*

Don't get caught up in why or why not, just let the relationship grow or end. If they don't seem to be willing to make time for you or to answer your questions, just move on to someone else.

Always show appreciation. This is key to building the relationship with a mentor. Ask one or two questions, then show your gratitude. Buy them a gift card for coffee or a restaurant. It could be for $5. The amount doesn't matter—the gesture is to show that you are serious and that you take their time very seriously.

Most people want to help others that appreciate and value them and their time. When you express gratitude verbally and through thank you cards, this demonstrates that you truly appreciate and value them, causing them to respond favorably more often.

Remember, you don't have to buy them something all the time or every time. It is the thought and demonstration of appreciation that matters.

## HOW DO YOU BECOME A MENTOR?

Be sensitive to the needs of others. Let them know that if they have any questions or would like to run something by you, you are available to them.

You can ask them questions every so often that have to do with their personal life and career. Give them encouragement on a regular basis. Offer to let them join you for training or to simply get together to chat.

When you encourage others and make yourself available, people will take you up on your offers. This will not happen with everyone, but you don't need to mentor everyone, just those who appreciate and respect your guidance and advice.

# ACTION PLAN

1. Write a list of 10-20 potential mentors.

2. Review this chapter 2-5 times.

3. Start reaching out and building a relationship with potential mentors.

4. Identify several up-and-coming firefighters.

5. Offer to train with them and let them know you are available to them if they want to train or if they have any questions.

6. Follow up with both groups regularly.

7. Offer to go to coffee or lunch and get to know them and understand their goals and ambitions— and share yours as well if you feel they are interested.

8. Listen to Firefighter Toolbox Podcast episode 061 - "Iron Sharpens Iron" (www.firefightertoolbox. com/061)

# Once we decide to stop learning, it's time to leave the fire service.

—David J. Soler

TACTIC #1

# ALWAYS BE A STUDENT OF FIREFIGHTING

# Don't ever hesitate to ask questions. If you don't understand the answer, ask the question again until you do understand the answer.

— Assistant Chief Robert C. Simmons
Firefighter Toolbox Podcast, Episode 016

One of the most attractive attributes of great and respected firefighters is the fact that they are always looking to learn and share. They know that the skill of firefighting is constantly evolving.

Developing the skills of learning, training, and teaching, and then using those skills regularly are what make firefighters great.

There is an extremely high chance that the equipment and gear we start our careers with will be obsolete when we retire or end our careers. A lot of the methodology or tactics may be obsolete as well.

Always be looking to learn, train, and teach/share regardless of your current position or level of experience. This is a key to greatness.

Remember that there are many ways to learn new information and skills. In today's age with podcasts, videos, books, booklets, ebooks, articles, blogs, in-house training, new equipment training, modern fire behavior advances, and other disciplines in the fire service like rescue, HAZMAT, fire prevention, instructor training, driver/operators, advanced fire firefighting tactics and skills, fire boat, shipboard firefighting, building construction, etc., there are almost endless (or so it seems) ways to learn and study in the fire service (not to mention the whole EMS side of the fire service).

So there will never be a shortage of things to learn and become competent in. The decision will be yours. Great and respected firefighters will always be looking to learn, train, and teach throughout their careers and even afterward.

## Every day you're getting better or worse. Which is it for you today?

— David J Soler
  Firefighter Toolbox

## FIREFIGHTER PREPLAN TIP

Turn your smart phone into a training phone. Get firefighter training podcasts, interviews, audio training programs, etc., and listen to them as you commute, work out or do chores. This is an extremely beneficial use of that time. If you commute just 30 minutes, four times a week, that is four hours of training per week and 200 hours per year, assuming you take two weeks off without listening.

That training time adds up and you will be amazed at how much you will learn with just this simple habit.

Visit some great firefighter training blogs like FirefighterToolbox.com or VentEnterSearch.com to read the weekly posts.

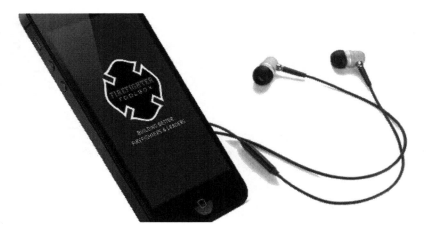

# ACTION PLAN

1. Review and study the Firefighter Training Success Diamond.

2. Is there any area of expertise where you skipped a base?

3. Pick an area of expertise you want to build in your career, and map out the plan with the Firefighter Training Success Diamond.

# Every call is a classroom. Be a student and be a teacher.

—David J. Soler

# MAKE EVERY CALL A CLASSROOM— BE A STUDENT/BE A TEACHER

. . . . . . . . . . . . . . . . . . . . . . . . . . . .

*Every day is training day. Therefore, every day
you have the opportunity to take another step
towards mastery.*

. . . . . . . . . . . . . . . . . . . . . . . . . . . .

Great firefighters approach every call as a classroom. There is always something to learn and something to teach. As an up-and-coming firefighter, always be looking to learn.

For calls that involve fires and rescues, obviously there is so much to learn, so keep your eyes open. Observe others and discuss the incident with your officers and senior firefighters after the call or during the rehab or overhaul.

Now, the key is to not stop there. What about the medical assist calls or personnel needed calls? Most calls we run now are EMS-related. So how can we train on those calls?

Take your skills to the next level by running scenarios in your head or with the crew.

## HERE'S HOW:

Imagine you have a fire at the incident you are headed to. Where's the hydrant? Which attack line would you grab? Which supply line is needed? What is your role on the scene?

What would you do if someone was trapped on the second floor?

Observe the roof and think about how to open the roof. What tools would you need?

What kind of building construction is the structure you are going to?

These are just samples of the multitude of questions you can ask yourself or crew. Then discuss them and research them to make sure you have the right answers. This is a way to make learning fun and pass the time on these not-so-exciting calls.

BCoFD E15 & T15 making this "Automatic Alarm" a classroom.
Operating as if there was a fire in the building.

Courtesy: Author - FirefighterToolbox.com

# ACTION PLAN

1. For the next 10 non-emergency calls, decide to make them a classroom.

2. Ask yourself strategy and tactics questions during the call. (Do not let this interfere with the call itself or your ability to do your job on the call.)

3. Discuss those tactics with your crew on the call or after.

4. Research the answers to your questions for verification.

TACTIC #3

# HAVE A GREAT FIREFIGHTER
# ATTITUDE

# Every day is an opportunity to build yourself into a better firefighter and person.

—David J. Soler

## EVERY DAY IS TRAINING DAY.

Every day we have the opportunity to take our skills to the next level. We have the opportunity to build on the foundation of respect we poured the day before. We have the opportunity to enhance our skills and abilities from the day before. We have the opportunity to plant more seeds of fire ground success to make the most of every day. That is what is meant when we say that *every day is training day*.

Also know this: *Great firefighters aren't born. They're built, one training at a time.*

Every day we have the opportunity to build ourselves into great firefighters. Let us continue to build every day. That is the habit of great firefighters. They are always building. Every day they build.

## TAKE NO SHORT CUTS BECAUSE THERE ARE NO SHORT CUTS.

Attitude is everything, because it's going to determine how long it takes you to become a good firefighter.

— Bryan T. Smith
  Firefighter Toolbox

There are no shortcuts to greatness and respect in the fire service. Know that it takes a lot of discipline and time to achieve the greatness you desire and to gain respect that comes from that discipline.

**There are no short cuts. Doing work is the DNA of a great firefighter.**

*Courtesy: Chief Gord Schreiner and Chief Les Karpluk - FirefighterToolbox.com*

Being respected as a firefighter and having a rewarding fire service career is a process that happens over time, not overnight. We will have to follow the natural process of consistent hard work and the growth that makes it possible. There are no short cuts and we will not receive instant gratification or respect. This isn't the lottery.

Great firefighters know they need to commit themselves to the constant and continuous process of improvement to reveal and harness their full potential.

Great firefighters don't lower their expectations to meet a poor performance. They raise their performance to meet the expectations.

Expect the best of yourself, and then do what is necessary to make it a reality.

. . . . . . . . . . . . . . . . . . . . . . . . . . . . . .

*Every day is training day. Therefore, every day you have the opportunity to take another step towards mastery.*

. . . . . . . . . . . . . . . . . . . . . . . . . . . . . .

# ACTION PLAN

1. Review this chapter.

2. Write out the key attitudes and mindsets.

3. Repeat them often to yourself.

4. Post them on your mirror, in your locker, etc., to continually remind yourself.

5. Check out and purchase the Firefighter Toolbox Training Challenge Coin. Let it serve as a reminder to train every day.

One of the best gifts we can receive in the fire service is a trusted mentor. One of the best gifts we can give is being a trusted mentor.

—David J. Soler

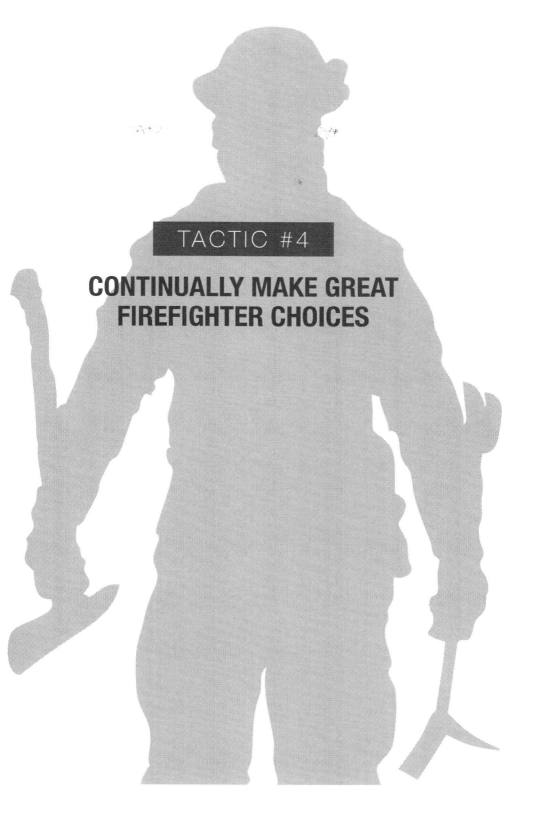

TACTIC #4

# CONTINUALLY MAKE GREAT FIREFIGHTER CHOICES

**Develop great habits early in your career and they will guide you well.**

*Courtesy: Rob Ramirez - FirefighterToolbox.com*

## GREAT HABITS START WITH GREAT CHOICES

Everything we are and are known for is because we first made a choice. Think back to when you rode the fire engine for the first time and then heard the federal siren, getting that rush that hooks us for life. It all started with a choice. Even those things that we wish we hadn't done started with a choice.

Our choices can take us to greatness or to ruin. Everything we become starts with a choice. Those same choices exercised consistently yield habits. Those habits build a reputation. That reputation is either a respectable one or a not-so-respectable one.

## *FIREFIGHTER PREPLAN* EQUATIONS:

Choices + Consistency = Habits

    Hence:

Great choices + Great Consistency = Great Habits

    Hence:

Great Habits = Great Reputation

    Which would also mean:

Bad Choices + Consistency = Bad Habits

    Concluding:

Bad Choices = Bad Habits

    Which then also means:

Respectable Choices + Consistency = Respectable Habits

    Hence:

Respectable Choices = Respectable Habits

    Which by conclusion:

Respectable Habits = Respectable Reputation

## Complacency can kill you. It has killed people and we need to be on our toes and prepared.

— Battalion Chief Joe Turner,
  City of Hoboken Fire Dept. (NJ)
  Firefighter Toolbox Podcast, Episode 001

If our goal is to become a respected firefighter (which we will call "RFF"), and if the way to become a RFF is to earn a respectable reputation, and if the way to earn a respectable reputation is to develop respectable habits and do them consistently, and if the way to develop repeatable habits is to make respectable choices consistently, then we can conclude that being a respectable firefighter starts with making respectable choices.

So, the little choices that we make thousands of times a day are what lead us to being a respected firefighter.

Great firefighters know this and therefore treat these choices, no matter how small, with the utmost respect and value because they lead to respect and greatness.

Choices like these:

- Do we show up early?
- Do we do our checks right away?
- Do we help with packing the hose?
- Do we train a little more each day?
- Do I lead by example?
- It's hot outside, do I still train?

- Nobody will know, but is it something I should do?
- Should I say this?
- Should I tell this person off?
- Should I insult this person?
- Should I eat that cake?
- Should I skip my workout today?
- Should I clean my gear now or later?
- Should I check my SCBA now or later?

These are the little questions that we make daily choices on. They are the seeds of being a great and respected firefighter. The choices we make with these and the other questions we ask ourselves will then lead us to habits and then to a reputation.

Which reputation do you want?

Either way, it all starts with your choices.

# ACTION PLAN

1. Review this chapter.

2. Decide that you will make conscious choices.

3. Realize that the small choices you are making will impact your reputation and career.

4. List any choices you want to improve on and/or maintain.

5. Make a checklist of these choices and track your progress.

# BUILD GREAT FIREFIGHTER HABITS

# Motivation gets us started and keeps us going. Great habits are like roots—they keep us growing in the right direction and sustain us long term.

—David J. Soler

Whenever we study and dissect great firefighters, we find great habits. Great habits are formed from your positive choices and actions done over and over again, whether someone is watching or not.

We are the sum of our habits. When we look at great firefighters, we will see that they have set up great health habits, great training habits, great thinking habits, great on-duty habits, great off-duty habits, etc.

Never will you find a great firefighter who just stumbled on it and became great. Firefighters learn from others, and through many other ways, which great habits need to be formed to be successful as a firefighter. They implemented and became a slave to those habits, doing them over and over and over again, so much so that the habit became part of who they were as firefighters.

Now, those habits are just second nature, and if the firefighter doesn't continue the habits, they will feel awkward or naked as though something is wrong or missing.

On the other side, if we study unsuccessful firefighters, we will find that they have poor habits. They may have a habit of being late or not studying. They may have a habit of being too busy to train or too focused on the things that aren't important, thereby distracting themselves from doing the important things consistently.

Great firefighters know the importance of great habits. They identify the habits of great firefighters and they implement those habits themselves. They marry those habits and continue them over and over, never stopping them unless they find a better one.

# FIREFIGHTER PREPLAN
# ACTION PLAN

1. Write a list of habits you would like to build into your career, then schedule them in. Below are some examples.

   Habit 1- 30 minutes/day to train and learn.

   Habit 2- Work out 3 times/week

   Habit 3- Always be 30 minutes early to work

   Habit 4- Appreciate someone daily

   Habit 5- (What will yours be?)

## TACTIC #6

# ALWAYS BE A GREAT TEAM PLAYER

**Firefighting is a team sport. Always be a great team player.**

*Courtesy: Chief Rob Evans and Chief Les Karpluk - FirefighterToolbox.com*

## FIREFIGHTING IS A TEAM SPORT

There are many things you can do alone in life and still be successful. However, firefighting is not one of them. It has nothing to do with your skills and abilities. It has to do with the nature of firefighting.

To be successful in the fire service, we have to understand and appreciate the fact that firefighting is a "team job" like a "team sport."

If we were to compare firefighting to sports, then American football would be a sport that aligns most similarly and tennis singles would be the most opposite.

To understand this concept of how important teammates are in the fire service, let's review American football (herein called football). Football is made up of many different positions. These positions need different skill sets and abilities and need to accomplish some unique tasks that other positions don't have to do.

For example, in football, there is a position called a *kicker*, who is the person responsible for kicking the ball to the other team, punting the ball to the other team, and kicking field goals. This person's skills and abilities and their position's roles and responsibilities are very different than the offensive line position that blocks the other team. The offensive line player never has to kick the ball and really doesn't even have to touch the ball unless it's a loose ball on the ground.

On the fire ground, we have positions such as pump operator whose job is to stay with the engine and pump the lines and provide water to the nozzle firefighter. This person needs to have certain knowledge, skills, and abilities specializing in that role. Once they are pumping the engine, they will not be doing any other role on the fire ground.

We have the incident commander (IC) who is managing the incident from the strategic level. They only participate on the fire ground in that facet. The IC would be like a coach in football. They call the plays, they watch what is happening, they make adjustments, but they don't go into the game.

Now, what's important to understand here is that the coach needs their football players just like the incident commander needs their firefighters. The pump operator needs the nozzle firefighter just as much as the quarterback needs the receiver. The nozzle firefighter needs the pump operator just as much as the receiver needs the quarterback.

Please evaluate these questions:

▶ How good is a quarterback without any receivers?
▶ How good is a receiver without a quarterback?

▶ How important is a quarterback and receiver without the offensive line blocking?

▶ How good are the players without the coach providing the plays, instruction, and coordination?

▶ How good is the coach without the players to run the plays?

## If you're looking for applause: join the circus. If you're looking to contribute, serve and make a difference in the lives of others: join the fire service.

—David J. Soler, *Firefighter Preplan*

In the fire service, there are many roles on the fire ground. All are important and most are critically important. If all of these positions are not filled, most of the other positions are worthless, just like in football.

The key to a successful career in the fire service is to learn quickly and remember often that no one position or firefighter is the game winner or hero. We accomplish anything and everything on the fire ground as a team.

If you are the person on the nozzle who is making the knock on the fire, remember that you need the help of the back-up firefighter, pump operator, hydrant firefighter, forcible-entry crew, etcetera.

If you are making the grab on a victim in the fire and bringing them to safety, remember that you need the driver to get you to the scene, the vent crew to vent, the attack crew to get the fire, the forcible-entry team, the incident commander, etc. Nothing on the fire ground is accomplished individually. So, always include your teammates when success is attained on the fire ground.

A big mistake, which happens often in the fire service, is when the firefighter thinks that they did it by themselves and that they deserve all the accolades. Don't let that person be you. Always share the accolades, especially if you are interviewed on the news.

If you ever get an award, let everyone know that it was *the team* that did the job and that you were just one part of the team. Knowing this and living this out is what builds camaraderie amongst your crew/department and builds respect and admiration for you.

Think about how you have seen this in some firefighters and how it made you respect them more. Then think about how you have *not* seen this in *other* firefighters who have taken all the credit and glory, and think about how you and/or others start to lose respect for them. Which one do you want to emulate?

Also, we can never achieve greatness without having a great team. If it's always all about you, then you will never achieve greatness.

We are only as good as our weakest link. On the fire ground, this is so vitally true. If we have a very weak engine crew, we will be very limited in how much searching we can do. If we have a very weak pump operator, it will weaken the fire attack crew.

So remember to train yourself up, but also those around you. This is a team sport and we will only go as far on the fire ground as our weakest link.

# ACTION PLAN

1. Know your role and perform it as if a video of your entire performance will be posted on YouTube. Perform like a champion!

2. If you get the exciting role like nozzle firefighter, always applaud the other members after the call for a job well done.

## TACTIC #7

# INCORPORATE THE 3 C'S OF GREAT FIREFIGHTERS

# Be the change you want to see in the fire service.

—Paraphrased from Mahatma Gandhi.

## COMMITMENT

## Know your job on the fire ground. Be committed to it and see it through to the end.

— Captain Bryan T. Smith
Firefighter Toolbox Podcast, Episode 003

## Failure is not an option.

— Michael Rehfeld
Firefighter Toolbox Podcast, Episode 007

Great firefighters are committed to being the best they can be. They are committed to the objective and mission on the fire ground and they are committed to their team.

This personal commitment goes above any oath they have taken. This commitment brings them respect from others.

When we are cold, wet, tired, and beat on the fire ground, do we pack it in or do with stick it out? (Great firefighters stick it out.)

When it's time to train or study, do we look for reasons to cancel the training or do we stay committed? (Great firefighters train and study.)

When it's time to pack up the hose bed, do we avoid it or are we there leading the way and contributing? (Great firefighters contribute.)

When things are not going our way, do we give up or continue on? (Great firefighters continue on.)

Committed firefighters stay committed and follow through on their assignments even when things are not going their way. They are dependable and stick it out, even if it's uncomfortable or just plain hard work. This is a choice. We all make choices in these situations and others like them. Great firefighters make the choice that shows their commitment to the craft and being the best firefighter and team member they can be. *They choose not to give up.* This commitment and mental toughness is valued and admired by firefighters.

## COMPASSION

### Some became firefighters for the benefits. We became firefighters so others can benefit.

—Firefighter Toolbox

Great firefighters have compassion. It gets really easy to become immune to other people's feelings. As firefighters, we see these types of situations all the time, whether it's another car fire, house fire, car accident, etc. We especially become immune to the typical, everyday calls we are accustomed to in our departments or districts.

The thing that great firefighters remember is that this is most likely the person's worst day of their life. It's not very often a firefighter's personal house catches on fire, although as firefighters, we go to other people's house fires all the time.

We go to car collisions all the time. Nonetheless, this could be very traumatic for the victim or the person involved in the incident. We don't know their background or how this will affect them emotionally.

The person's life may be altered dramatically, even though we think it's no big deal because we see it five times a week. The cost and inconvenience of minor fires and incidents compared to the cost and life-altering moments for the people involved in these incidents are not always understood or appreciated by firefighters.

Great firefighters show compassion. Even when it's our fifth fender-bender call on the shift, we are tired of writing reports, and we have to go back to write another report, great firefighters show compassion and understanding to those involved.

Here is a scenario: we were having one of those busy shifts where we were "running the wheels off the wagon" on multiple calls. We didn't get to rest and we didn't get to eat. The calls were mostly "junk calls" which were time-consuming and very high on the adrenaline scale.

## Do not look down on anyone unless you are helping them up.

—Division Chief Walt Lewis

I remember on one of the last calls of the shift, we were called for an "odor of burning." When we got there, we could hardly smell anything. I remember smelling more smoke and odor from our gear than in this dwelling.

Nevertheless, the woman was very emotional and she was almost in a state of panic. I remember the captain at the time stood with the occupant and listened and listened. He understood her concern and had compassion for her fears. She had an infant and wanted to ensure that the baby would not die in the middle of the night, etc. The captain, realizing this, explained to her that we would check the whole house with detectors that would tell us if there was anything in the air, even if we couldn't smell it.

We checked all the systems, including the hot water heater, duct work, attic, basement, stove, etc. At the end of the call, he acknowledged her feelings and explained that if he was in her situation, he would want the same thing done.

We took the extra time and energy as a crew and showed compassion for her concerns and fears. We verified the home was safe, checked all of her detectors, and provided her the security she needed. Some say this is great customer service, and I believe it is, but more importantly, this is showing compassion for the people we serve.

We pretty much knew within the first five minutes that there was no issue with the home. We were hungry and tired. This was the moment we got to decide whether to show compassion and commitment or to be short and frank and move on.

This is just a quick example about showing compassion for minor emergencies and false alarms. If we can show compassion on these types of calls and situations, how much more compassion will we need when major travesties occur?

Great firefighters show compassion throughout the day and throughout all calls.

## COURAGE

## For some, it's a job. For us, it's a calling.

—Firefighter Toolbox

Firefighting is a team activity and it is also one that requires us to be put in harm's way. Being courageous is not going on a suicide mission on the fire ground. Being courageous is putting ourselves in harm's way in as safe and smart a manner as possible.

We as firefighters must know the inherent dangers we face. We must be educated and aware of the challenges on the fire ground. We must remember how fellow brother and sister firefighters have lost their lives both courageously on the fire ground as well as in the unfortunate blunders that take lives.

Once educated on these things, we will still be faced with decisions on the fire ground and wherever else there is the need for us to risk our safety. Again, this risk must be a calculated risk and not a suicide mission.

We don't just sacrifice firefighters or ourselves to get a medal of honor. We take calculated risks that allow for us to save lives.

We know that we can do everything right on the fire ground and still someone can get killed. That is part of the job of being a firefighter. This is the job of firefighting. It doesn't matter if you are receiving a paycheck or not. What we need to know is that the fire doesn't care if you receive a paycheck or not, and it can kill us even if we do everything right.

So, there is a need for firefighters to be courageous. When the public calls 911, they expect the fire department to show up in spite of the dangers and to mitigate the emergency, doing everything possible to save the lives of those involved—just short of going on a suicide mission.

Great firefighters understand this and accept it. They know that they will be expected to go into harm's way to save someone and it could cost them their gear, their health, or even their life.

Great firefighters rely on their training, experience, skills, and abilities, as well as their gear and tools of the trade, to determine what an acceptable risk is for the reward. They do not go on suicide missions, but they often put themselves in harm's way with a calculated strategy.

There have been a lot of work and studies done and research obtained that explain the risk-versus-reward for fire ground strategy and tactics. This is an area great firefighters continually study to be aware of what is happening around the country, not just in their local departments.

Some key points to know are that the risk must be worth the reward. We don't risk our lives to save a car or a house. We don't ruin a million-dollar apparatus for a $20,000 car. However, we do make a calculated risk with our equipment and such for saving a life, but we don't take ill-advised risks with firefighters' lives just to save property.

We perform calculated strategies and tactics which we believe will succeed to save a life. If we don't feel the strategy or tactic will work and we know that the mission cannot be accomplished safely, then we have the moral and ethical obligation to not perform that strategy or tactic on the fire ground.

Courage is knowing these facts and understanding the risk versus reward benefits and then making the best strategic and tactical decision and implementing it. Sometimes the most courageous tactic is to decide not to perform a rescue, because we know it will most likely kill us or other firefighters. Those are the toughest and most challenging decisions to accept. We always want to do something.

Sometimes you are on a call and are ordered out of the burning building, but you know there is a firefighter trapped inside. Sometimes the building is collapsing or partially collapsing. Sometimes the fire has gotten too far out of control and we have to back out. These are the toughest calls, especially when that downed firefighter has given the mayday and is communicating on the radio.

These situations require a tremendous amount of courage for both the incident commander and the firefighters. It knocks the wind out of us, knowing that we have to surrender at that moment and regroup. If we go after the mayday firefighter, we too will most likely be killed. Yet, if we do nothing, our fellow firefighter will die. This takes the most courage I have ever seen in life.

We can review some of these types of incidents; such as the Hackensack, New Jersey, Ford dealership fire, 9/11, and many others. They can be large or small, paid or volunteer, from various parts of the country and throughout the history of the fire service.

Courage is not just about running into the fire, but it is also sometimes about staying out. Courage could be running in and making the grab and it could be sharing our feelings after a traumatic loss, like when a child dies in our hands because our efforts didn't work.

Great firefighter's have courage and demonstrate courage.

# Be the firefighter who everyone has to say, "Stop working so hard, you're making the rest of us look bad."

— Lieutenant Jim Moss
Firefighter Toolbox Podcast, Episode 061

# ACTION PLAN

1. Always show compassion. What is routine or non-emergency for us, is the worst day of that person's life most often.

2. Choose to go the extra mile and stay committed.

3. Be educated on risk versus reward on the fire ground and be courageous. (Courageous means sometimes not going into the fire.)

We've got to look past man, women, black, white, Latino, gender roles, and things like that. We've got to look past that and we've got to look at people getting the job done.

— Division Chief Johnny Winston, Jr.
   Firefighter Toolbox Podcast, Episode 041

# BE LIKE THE FIRE: NON-BIASED

**We all have the same color blood. Being accepted
as a firefighter is all about whether or not you can do the job.**

*Courtesy: Div. Chief Johnny Winston, Jr. -
FirefighterToolbox.com and City of Madison FD, WI.*

Great and respected firefighters are biased, but not based on skin color, sex, nationality, socioeconomics, etc.

They simply want to know: Can you do the job of firefighting or not?

That is what counts. At your current level, can we count on you to do what is requested?

Here is the bottom line: If *you* can do the job and are willing to work, then *you* can be a firefighter. Don't believe or let anyone tell you that just because you are African American, Hispanic, female, volunteer (or fill in the blank) that *you* cannot do the job.

I have personally interviewed and witnessed many great and respected fire service leaders who have blazed the trail, are well-respected, and have accomplished, admirable careers. I have interviews with them on the Firefighter Toolbox Podcast and I have interviewed them for this book.

The bottom line for you being a firefighter is found in these questions:

*Can you do the job physically, mentally, and emotionally?*
*Are you willing to work hard and build your skills?*
*Are you willing to work hard on the fire ground and in the fire station?*
*Are you willing to keep learning about the ever-evolving skills of firefighting?*

If you answered "yes" to these questions and are willing to continually say "yes" to these questions, then you belong. You are a firefighter!

If you answered "no" to any of these questions, then you probably don't belong as a firefighter. The fire doesn't care if you are volunteering or getting a paycheck for being at the fire. It doesn't care if you are male or female, or black or white, and it doesn't care if you are new to firefighting or have 20 years in the service. It will kick your butt!

Unfortunately, LODD report data has shown that firefighters have lost their lives in all of those categories.

So you may hear throughout your career how "*volunteers get killed because they don't know what they're doing,*" but then career firefighters get killed, too. You may hear that "*these new rookies get killed because they are lacking experience,*" but then the 20-year veteran gets killed.

Study the numbers and read the reports, because they are not just numbers. They are people with families and with crews who went to the fire with them. They are firefighters who loved the fire service, just like you.

So the next time someone says that so-and-so can not do the job because of some biased reason, remember that firefighters have lost their lives in the fire service from every one of the categories just mentioned and firefighters have become chiefs from every category as well. Don't buy into the B.S. and don't think you are safe on the fire ground because of your category either.

The real questions are:

*Can you do the job of firefighting or not?*
*Can we count on you?*
*Are you going to be ready when called upon?*
*When it gets tough, are you not going to quit or give up?*

These are the questions we judge ourselves and other firefighters on so we can be best prepared for what we face, individually and as a team.

# ACTION PLAN

1. Work hard on your skills and certifications.

2. Work hard at the fire station and on the fire ground.

3. Work hard on your health, strength, and conditioning.

4. Ignore the bigots, racists, sexists, etc.

5. Be ready when called upon.

# Ultimately, as we all know in the fire service, somebody's life depends on you doing your job.

—Michael Rehfeld
Firefighter Toolbox Podcast,
Episode 007

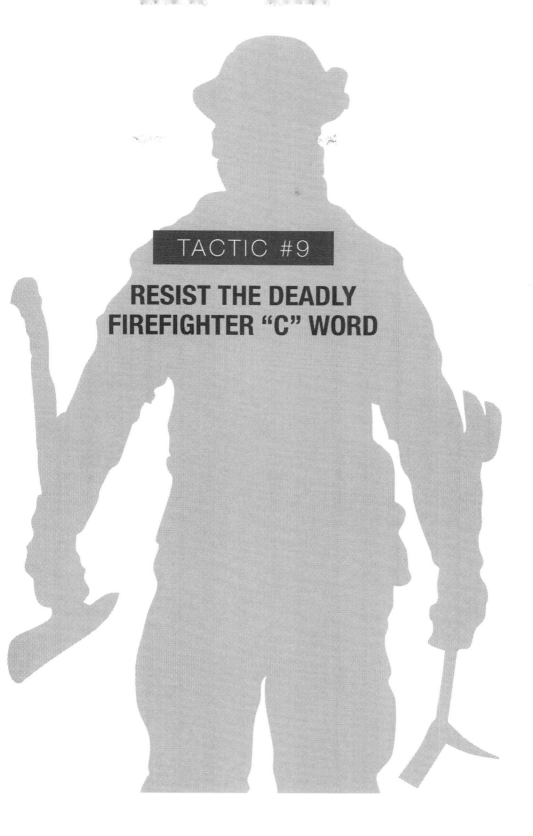

## TACTIC #9

# RESIST THE DEADLY FIREFIGHTER "C" WORD

## COMPLACENCY

> Complacency can kill you. It has killed people, and you need to be on your toes and prepared.
>
> — Battalion Chief Joe Turner
> Firefighter Toolbox Podcast, Episode 001

Complacency is one of the things that we all struggle with if we keep doing anything for a long period of time. Firefighting is no different. Complacency creeps up on us: we may skip a training, we may get too busy, we may get bored. Complacency is right there to jump on us and hurt us.

Never become complacent on the fire ground, because that is how we get seriously hurt or killed. Treat every call like it's the Super Bowl— be alert and situationally aware.

**Never get complacent.**

*Courtesy: Sean Wilson*

222

# FIVE WAYS TO BEAT COMPLACENCY AROUND THE FIREHOUSE

### 1. Continue to set goals to improve.

Continuing to set goals encourages us to stretch ourselves out of our comfort zones—which is where we can become complacent. What goals can you set to continue to grow as a firefighter?

### 2. Change up the routine.

Routines are great and vital in the fire service. Sometimes a training routine can turn into complacency if we are always working on the same skills or in the same environment. Look for ways to change up the environment, such as training at different locations or in different weather conditions. Change up the training scenarios or personnel.

### 3. Bring in new firefighters to train with.

Asking new firefighters to train with you gives the training a different feel. It allows those who were students to become teachers and changes the dynamics of the training.

### 4. Bring in different firefighters to train with.

Going to train with other companies or departments keeps the training fresh, exciting, and fun. We are a brotherhood/sisterhood, therefore training with mutual aid companies as well as friends you meet at certification trainings or conferences is fun and rewarding.

Look to meet new firefighters and train with them. It's invaluable.

### 5. Learn ways to make it a fun or friendly training competition.

One of the best training tools is a stopwatch. Timing the evolutions is a great way to track your progress on how quick and proficient you or your crew are becoming. It's also a great way to have a friendly competition with either yourself or with your crew.

For example, set up an evolution to stretch the 1 ¾-inch hand line, properly set it up for an interior attack, and charge the line. See how long it takes from start to flowing water. Next, see if you can beat your time or have crew 2 see if they can beat your time. You can do this with pretty much any skill or evolution. Remember to ensure all safety precautions.

# AVOID THE 4 RESPECT-KILLERS
# FOR FIREFIGHTERS

# Laziness is a choice. It's a very bad choice.

—Firefighter Preplan

Let this be your warning. You can kill your reputation, or build a negative reputation, much faster than you can build a positive reputation. These "4 L's" are actions that will kill your reputation in a hurry. These seem to be unwritten rules in the fire service, and unfortunately some firefighters never learn them. So I will share them here so you know them and can be warned and informed.

## RESPECT KILLER #1: BEING LATE

Firefighters are not late. If you believe you are a firefighter, or if you want to be a firefighter and hope to be a great one, then "late" is something you will never be. The question is this: *How early will you be?*

How early do you arrive for your shift? How early do you arrive for your training? How early do you arrive for cleaning the station? Get in a habit of being very early. Therefore, if you do happen to run a little late, you will still arrive early or on time.

Every department has a norm for what is expected. My department has the norm of being one-hour early for your shift. Almost everybody follows the one-hour early "unwritten rule" so it is fair for everyone. Some don't do this, and are negatively known as "one of them."

As a rookie or an up-and-coming firefighter, you should be energized, excited to get to work, and be there ready to go. Showing up late is a career-killer. Remember, you are now always early; it's just about learning *how early* to show up. Do this and you will not have trouble with your reputation or lose respect.

## RESPECT KILLER #2: BEING LAST

Firefighters are not last. We strive to be "first-due" and "first-in". No great firefighter wants to be last. Great firefighters are team players and no matter when they arrive at the fire scene, they go to work.

Here is the thing you need to know as a rookie firefighter or up-and-coming firefighter: don't be last. Don't be last to the station. Don't be last to pack the hose up after the call. Don't be last to do house cleaning. Don't be last when the officer calls a meeting. Don't be last when getting on the apparatus to go on the call. Don't be last to training. Don't be last to open the books.

In fact, these are all things in which you must strive to be first. First to pack the hose. First to clean the dishes. First to train. First to get on the apparatus, etcetera.

The only thing that is respectable for a rookie to be "*last-in*" is the food line. Let your officers and crew eat first. Make sure you're last when it comes to eating and sitting on the couch.

## RESPECT KILLER #3: BEING LOST

Getting lost on the fire ground is a no-no. If you're an up-and-coming firefighter, you must stick with your partner or officer like they are your SCBA. Do not be more than an arm's length away. You are to be watching them and studying them constantly. Do not daydream and do not stray.

The other no-no is being lost in the fire station. When the captain or senior firefighter has to look for you, it is an issue. Do not wander away or hideout in the fire station. When you are at the fire station, you are there to work.

Have the mindset that you are to work every single minute you are there unless the captain or senior firefighter tells you to take a break.

Always be available and in plain sight. If you need to go somewhere, like to make a phone call, let someone know. For example, say something like, "Hey Captain, I have to make a family phone call. Is now a good time? I'll be about 15 minutes, and I'll be out on the back pad if that's okay?"

This will allow the senior firefighter or captain to know where you are and what you are doing. It will also allow them to teach you about the station routine. They may say, "No, we are getting ready to clean up. You can call at 11 AM, unless it's an emergency."

This will keep you in the good graces and, again, will protect you from being late for cleanup, which is Respect Killer #2.

## RESPECT KILLER #4: LAZINESS

Laziness is a choice. It's a very bad choice. Firefighters are the opposite of lazy. They are hard-working, dedicated, selfless, firefighting machines. If you want to build a reputation of being a great firefighter, I encourage you to be allergic to "laziness." Make it like a peanut allergy: if you choose to eat it, you might die.

Look to work your tail off. Look to be a major contributor when packing hose, cleaning equipment, having your gear ready, and cleaning the firehouse. Whatever needs to be done, find out and do it, or be a major contributor to the job.

Make it a routine that people have to tell you to take a break. It's better if your captain tells you to take a break than it is for your captain to tell you to get off your butt to do something.

# ACTION PLAN

1. Become *allergic* to being LATE. Be very early.

2. Become *allergic* to being LAZY. Don't be lazy, work hard all the time, always be looking to work and be active.

3. Become *allergic* to being LAST. Be first, not last.

4. Become *allergic* to being LOST. Always let your officer/senior firefighter know where you are and what you are doing.

# ELIMINATE THE TOP 3 MOST-HATED FIREFIGHTER BEHAVIORS IN YOURSELF

# The fire ground is dangerous and risky enough without our help. Be smart, be aggressive, and be safe. Move with purpose.

—David J. Soler

As firefighters, we always love getting something for free, like when people drop off free food at the fire station or someone is giving out free t-shirts at a conference. In fact, there is an expression around the fire station that says, "If it's free, give me three."

Here is where a new rookie or an up-and-coming firefighter can get confused. We firefighters may love to get some things for free, but we absolutely do not want the following three "free's."

In fact, these are the top three most-hated firefighter behaviors. Starting the countdown with:

## #3: FREELOADING

### Definition: *Freeloader*
*to take advantage of others for free food, entertainment, etc. (dictionary.com)*

A freeloader is someone who is always eating the station food and using the station supplies, using the station cable TV or Internet, but never contributing to the station kitty (the funds to replenish the food and supplies). This is someone who is always asking for a favor, but never returning the favor.

A freeloader is someone who asks to do exchange work for some emergency, but when it's time to repay the favor, they always seem to be unable to work the day that they owe someone else.

A freeloader consistency asks to "holdover" on a shift or asks you to come in early, but then doesn't repay the favor. They usually come up with great reasons because they have mastered the art of freeloading.

Recognize this behavior and do not do it. There are no free lunches in the fire service and there are no free shift exchanges. Always pay your way, and in fact, pay a little extra.

## #2: FREEWHEELING

### Definition: *Freewheeler*

1 - *A person who works or lives in an independent, often daring, way. (dictionary.com)*
2 - *Someone acting freely or even irresponsibly. (thefreedictionary.com)*

Firefighting is a team sport. We work together as a team and we protect and save each other as a team. When a firefighter starts acting like a freewheeler, they jeopardize the safety of the crew they are with or others on the fire ground.

A freewheeler takes unnecessary risks, and this is unacceptable. As firefighters, we know that we may be a person's last chance for safety and survival. We take this very seriously, and we are willing to put ourselves in harm's way, but we are not willing to be stupid about it. We take calculated risks, and we are prepared for them. We don't take high-risk, low-chance-of-success options (or "risk a lot to save a little") on the fire ground.

Do not be a "freewheeler" on the fire ground, because you are an accident or catastrophe waiting to happen.

234

# #1: FREELANCING

### Definition: *Fire Ground Freelancing*

*Knowingly or unknowingly, not doing your assigned role and assignment on the fire ground and/or choosing without proper authority to do another role or assignment on the fire ground or none at all. (Defined by Firefighter Preplan)*

Freelancing on the fire ground is the #1 most-hated behavior by firefighters. Firefighting is a team sport. We all have a job to do on the fire ground. There is this code that is understood on the fire ground about standard operating guidelines. We as firefighters will look to help a fellow brother/sister firefighter out all the way except when they desert the team and start freelancing.

Anytime someone freelances on the fire ground, they are jeopardizing someone's life. If your job is to throw the ground ladder to the second floor, you need to do it without hesitation. If your job is to shut off the utilities, you need to do it because someone else is risking their life, **trusting** that it is getting done. When the "sh*t hits the fan," that job needs to be done because firefighters' lives are depending on it.

For example, we have fire on the first floor and the search firefighter goes in quickly to get to the second floor to check for a report of someone trapped. They know that the chance of the stairs being there on the way down are slim. Therefore, this firefighter is expecting to go out the window via the ground ladder that the outside vent (OV) firefighter is going to do as pre-assigned.

But what if the OV firefighter decides to let the driver throw the ladder and goes to search the basement?

That could easily create a possible firefighter "mayday" situation for the search firefighter on the second floor because the driver is raising the aerial to the roof. I don't have to tell you how it ends because these situations happen all the time. Just go ask someone about a situation in your department where something went badly or almost went badly because of freelancing. You will easily see the disdain for it.

Situations like these happen all too often on the fire ground and the only thing saving our butts is that other firefighters pick up the slack and get the job done.

The lesson here is to not freelance. Know your role on the fire ground and do it. Failure is not an option. We have no time for excuses or stories. If your job is to throw the ground ladder, then throw the ground ladder. If your job is to feed hose, then feed the hose. If your job is to establish a water supply, then establish a water supply. Period. End of story.

Take this to heart, because if you are seriously interested in having a great career, freelancing is not something you ever want to participate in.

## KNOW THE ROLES AND RESPONSIBILITIES

Study your standard operating guidelines or manual of guidelines. Know the roles of the first in engine, second in engine, third in engine, etc. Know your job and your role on the fire ground.

Know your seating assignment or job within your apparatus. Are you the hydrant firefighter? Are you the nozzle firefighter? Are you the back-up firefighter? What is your role? Know this before you ever get to the scene. If you're a career firefighter, you should be assigned a position with roles and responsibilities for your shift. If you're a volunteer, it is usually seating assignments that determine your roles and responsibilities.

This chapter isn't to teach all the roles and responsibilities of firefighters and seating assignments. It is to share an overview of the importance of always knowing your role and responsibilities and doing it, which are the opposite of freelancing.

At any point going to a call or on a call, you must know what your role and responsibilities are. Then be ready to do them or be doing them. If you don't know, then you are freelancing or getting ready to freelance.

**Always know your role and do your job on the fire ground. No freelancing.**

Photo of Baltimore County Fire Dept.
Courtesy: Capt. Bryan T. Smith - FirefighterToolbox.com

# ACTION PLAN

1. Review this chapter

2. Examine your behavior(s) over the last 3-6 months and see if you have participated in these behaviors (freelancing, freeloading, freewheeling).

3. If you have identified some from #2, then work to eliminate them quickly.

4. Study your standard operating guidelines, roles, and responsibilities to be certain you know them. Study them and commit them to memory.

5. Review with an officer or senior firefighter your roles and responsibilities for different calls and seating assignments. Commit them to memory.

6. Make sure you know how to perform your roles and responsibilities and/or start training on them as soon as possible.

TACTIC #12

# ELIMINATE THE 3 DESTRUCTIVE C'S TO A FIRE SERVICE CAREER

# If you're not part of the solution, then you are part of the problem.

—David J. Soler

# CRITICIZE, CONDEMN, AND COMPLAIN

. . . . . . . . . . . . . . . . . . . . . . . . . . . . .

*Great firefighters focus on*
*what's right, not who is right.*

. . . . . . . . . . . . . . . . . . . . . . . . . . . . .

The easiest things to do in the fire service are to criticize, condemn, and complain—we call those the destructive 3 C's. Some people in the fire service criticize, condemn, and complain like there is an award for it. They never stop and are always looking for more ways to do it. In fact, it can be argued that some in the fire service have earned a PhD degree for complaining.

> Firefighting both on the fire ground and off is a team activity. We succeed better when we all contribute.

However, when we study great firefighters, we find they are encouraging, focused on getting the best for everyone, and focused on the positive. These individuals are the problem-solvers, not problem-creators.

How do great firefighters handle bad ideas or bad situations that have been presented or implemented? They shift their focus to alternate and better solutions. They realize that the person who had the bad idea at least had the courage and desire to think of something and try to implement it. They are trying to solve an issue or improve something.

That is commendable and they applaud the person for that. What they would do, instead of shooting down the idea, is to focus on the person's intent—the problem that they were trying to solve. Then they look for more

241

solutions and/or better ideas, allowing everyone to come to a consensus that it will be better or at least worth a try.

In the fire service, we are a paramilitary organization that has to answer to authority and follow commands. It is imperative to follow commands unless it causes a severe risk or death to oneself or the crew. In this book, I am not talking about situations on the fire ground during the urgency of the matter and the command structure we have to follow. That is another discussion and book. We are talking about the other 95% of the time that organizations, officers, administrators, etc., make bad decisions or implement bad policies.

What I am sharing here are the ideas and decisions around the fire station and the non-emergency interactions between fellow officers or fellow crews. Things such as waxing the floors every day or how we conduct trainings or how we speak of our company.

The key takeaway here is to avoid the destructive 3 C's. If you criticize, condemn, and complain, you will lose respect from others. Look for ways to be solution-oriented. Focus on what the person is trying to achieve versus the faults you see in solution that they presented. Seek to understand what their goal is and provide other ways to help them achieve it.

Be willing to try the new idea fairly and get honest results from it. Our initial skepticism may be wrong: some ideas that we think are not good may work sometimes.

As an up-and-coming firefighter or officer, eliminate the destructive 3 C's from your skill set. The last thing you want to be known for is the person who always complains, criticizes, and condemns. That is the quickest way to being shunned by others.

How do you deal with people in your firehouse or on your rig that have the destructive 3 C's? The most important thing we can do is to not be "that guy/girl." Don't be the one who is criticizing, complaining, or condemning. If you catch yourself doing this, stop immediately. Then point to the positive and start being part of the solution.

If someone on your shift or crew is partaking in the destructive 3 C's, here is what I recommend:

Ask them if they realize that they are criticizing, complaining, or condemning.

1. If they say "no," then communicate with them about the dangers of this behavior and how they're not helping the team or themselves. Provide them with solutions to not partake in the destructive 3 C's and how they can solve for whatever they are criticizing, complaining, or condemning.

   Ask them to think and share ideas that can solve the issues at hand or improve upon the situation to make it satisfactory.

2. If they say "yes," ask them what they hope to attain by criticizing, complaining, or condemning.

   Then ask them what they think the solution would be and how they can be a part of it, especially since the criticizing, complaining, or condemning isn't going to work.

# ACTION PLAN

1. Eliminate the 3 destructive C's (criticizing, complaining, condemning) from your mindset/behavior.

2. Focus on the solution and go to work on it.

3. Focus on what is right and not who is right or wrong.

TACTIC #13

**ONLY USE THE RADIO
FOR THESE 4 REASONS**

One thing that new or up-and-coming firefighters get confused on is when and why to use the radio. Unfortunately, most senior officers are not the most proficient at it and do not provide a great example. Use the following information as a guide, but check with your department's operating guidelines.

Our goal is to keep the airwaves open, meaning very little talking on the radio. We need to keep our radio traffic to a minimum in case someone gets hurt or calls a mayday. If they do, they will be heard, acknowledged, and responded to quickly. Unfortunately, lots of incidents get multiple people talking—sometimes for extensive durations. When someone is talking on the radio, it means that no one else can use the radio to call for help.

## HERE ARE THE 4 REASONS TO USE THE RADIO:
### (IN NO PARTICULAR ORDER)

### 1. To provide vital information

**Providing the Brief Initial Report is
one of the most valuable uses of the radio.**

*Photo of Baltimore County Fire Dept.
Courtesy: Capt. Bryan T. Smith - FirefighterToolbox.com*

*Use the radio to provide key information about the safety and objectives of the incident.*

## EXAMPLES INCLUDE:

- Unit is en route
- Providing the brief initial report (B.I.R.)
- Providing a conditions-actions-needs report (C.A.N.)
- Notification of victim found
- Notification of signs of collapse

## 2. To provide vital instructions

**David J. Soler operating as Incident Commander:
Listening and providing vital instructions via the radio.**

Use the radio to provide instructions and/or directions needed that are not already dictated by our arrival sequence, seating assignment, SOGs, or if a change needs to be directed.

247

## EXAMPLES INCLUDE:

- Driver telling the hydrant firefighter to send the water
- The incident commander (I.C.) instructing a crew to do an additional task
- The I.C. instructing another engine to lay an additional supply line

## 3. As a lifeline

The #1 reason we carry a radio is for safety. It's our lifeline if anything goes wrong. The sooner we call for help or send a "mayday," the greater chance we have of living through the situation.

## EXAMPLES INCLUDE:

- When you are trapped or hurt and need assistance in the hot zone
- When you're in a jam
- When you think you're in a jam

*Make sure you know how to call a mayday and have practiced it before you go on fire calls where you will be making entry.

### Calling the Mayday: Quick Overview*

Step 1 -  Click up and say, "Mayday, Mayday, Mayday!"

Step 2 -  Provide your L.U.N.A.R. (location, unit, name, air, resources needed)

Step 3 -  Provide a "C.A.N." report.

Step 4 -  Repeat if unacknowledged by the I.C.

Step 5 -  Thump the floor or wall with a tool to help firefighters locate you.

248

*This is a suggestion. Know and follow your department's operating guidelines when calling a mayday.*

## 4. To listen and gather information

This is very important for the up-and-coming firefighter to learn. Listen to the radio at all times to always be aware of what is happening on the fire ground. Constantly be listening in on the fire ground channel for updates, transmissions, "maydays," C.A.N. reports, additional commands from the I.C., etc. *Always be listening.*

If you find yourself needing to use the radio for one of the above reasons, then follow the rules for speaking on the radio.

**Rule #1** -   Always be pithy* when communicating on the radio.
**Rule #2** - Always remember and do Rule #1.

*Pithy = Brief, concise, and forcefully expressive; succinct, compact, to the point.*

## THE IMPORTANCE OF RADIO TRAINING

Next, I will share with you one of the biggest mistakes firefighters make. They do not train on how to talk on the radio. We don't get the training or opportunity in the academy and, most likely, rarely get it at our stations. Therefore, you will notice that there is huge room for improvement throughout the fire service.

**Mistakes**: Firefighters and officers communicating on the radio who are: unreadable and garbled, too long-winded, very hyped-up, excited, and scream on the radio.

Again, this is advanced tactics of great firefighters. I have practiced and trained for communicating on the radio as a firefighter and incident commander, so I can speak on the radio like others who have training and experience—that is, very calm and pithy. Training also taught me how to speak on the radio while on air and I learned how to make it sound very understandable.

Because there are numerous different SCBA manufacturers, radio manufacturers, and different department lingo, it is hard for me to tell you how to do it exactly for yourself. This is something you will have to study by learning your department's radio communication lingo and commands, then learn your equipment and practice while using your equipment.

**NOTE: *This should be obvious, but do this training on a training channel and notify dispatch and all officers or departments that need to be aware that you are testing the radio and doing radio training. Have the proper permission to do this. Follow your departments SOGs for practicing radio communication.*

For example, after you have practiced your department's radio commands and know what to say on the radio, go on air and then talk on the radio. Have the crew in the kitchen of the firehouse with the officer. Then have a firefighter in the engine bay, or at any distance away where you can *only* hear them with the radio. Have the firefighter go on air, and have the officer in the kitchen call the firefighter on the radio. The firefighter on air can then respond. Everyone in the kitchen listening will be able to tell how clearly and understandable the firefighter is communicating.

**Step 1 -** The officer instructs the firefighter to speak with the mic to their throat.

**Step 2 -** The officer instructs the firefighter to speak with the mic to the face piece voice amplifier (if applicable).

**Step 3 -** The officer instructs the firefighter to speak another way. Doing this type of training, the officer and crews listening can hear firsthand which method works best for your equipment.

**Step 4 -** Do something to raise your heart rate and increase your breathing (like climbing stairs quickly or doing jumping jacks) to simulate fire ground operation heart rate and breathing. Then repeat steps 1–3 while your breathing is heavy.

The purpose of this drill is to learn to use your equipment, know how it works, and how you will sound on the radio. You can make adjustments as necessary, but you will learn with confidence the best way for you to communicate on the radio with your equipment and while operating on air.

Then learn your department's radio lingo and you will be in great shape for communicating on the radio on the fire ground.

If you can record it in training, it is a tremendous benefit to the person doing the talking on-air. They will be able to listen to themselves and be able to make adjustments or try different ways to communicate more effectively. Using a smartphone is the easiest and quickest way to record this training.

# ACTION PLAN

1. Review this chapter.

2. Become confident on when and how to use the radio by doing the radio training drill explained in this chapter.

3. Practice using the radio and radio terminology before you have to use it on the fire ground.

4. Ask your officers to do radio training with you. In the fire station, go on-air and practice communicating: giving C.A.N. reports and a L.U.N.A.R.
   *Be sure to be on-air AND have your full PPE on with gloves when training.

5. Practice with your face piece covered to simulate no visibility.

6. Practice while lying on the ground as if you fell or broke a leg. Have weight/hoses/mannequin put on top of you to simulate a ceiling or debris that fell on top of you.

# ADAPT AND LIVE BY THE
# SUCCESSFUL FIREFIGHTER MOTTO

## ADAPT AND OVERCOME

The fire service and the skill of firefighting are ever-evolving. The materials in our homes and offices are changing, which means fire behavior and fire science is changing. Our technology improves so our equipment improves. We are asked to do more with less because of budget restraints. The key thing to understand is that change is inevitable.

The successful firefighter has the motto of "Adapt and Overcome" whenever faced with a challenge—whether it's on the fire ground, in the fire station or with changes in the fire service. Always adapt and always overcome. It seems like nothing goes according to plan in the fire service, so always tell yourself to "adapt to it" and overcome it.

## ADAPTING AND OVERCOMING IN ACTION

We got alerted for a structure fire and when we arrived, we had a working structure fire. We needed a water supply, but the hydrant firefighter, let's call him John, could not get the hydrant caps off. He did everything he was supposed to do, but the caps were frozen on there. This was on an average day, so the weather should not have been a factor. (Although a little hydrant maintenance could have prevented it.)

The hydrant firefighter radioed command indicating the issue and to get another water supply, which the incident commander instructed the next arriving engine to do.

*What Happened Next?*

The hydrant firefighter didn't give up on their role and responsibilities. He kept at it, trying to get the caps off. In fact, he ended up taking a sledge hammer and pounding the (dry) hydrant. The thought process was that one of two things was going to happen. Either the hydrant caps were going to come off and they were going to establish a water supply, or they were going to break that hydrant and put it out of service where it should have been.

The good news is that the stubborn hydrant yielded and gave up those hydrant caps, and we were able to get the water supply established. We also had the second water supply established moments later.

Some great lessons here were that this firefighter knew his role and continued even though things didn't go as planned. This was something not learned or practiced at the academy. He adapted to the situation and overcame it. He knew that failure was not an option and that a water supply had to be established.

John, the hydrant firefighter, informed the incident commander of the situation, but continued with his role and assignment. He didn't give up.

How many times have others just said, "Ah, I guess it isn't going to work. I'll just stop or forget about it and go do something else?" Too many times, but don't let it be you.

Don't be that firefighter. Don't have *that* attitude. Know your role and your assignment. Know that challenges are coming. Be ready for them and not surprised by them. When something happens, just smile and say to yourself, "This is what David told me about in *Firefighter Preplan*." Then *THRIVE* through the challenge by adapting and overcoming. Use your knowledge, tools, and desire to make it happen. That's what the greats do, and I believe in you and know that you can do it, too!

# ACTION PLAN

1. Think about a scenario where you might have given up too soon.

2. Think about 3 more options you could do if that same scenario happens on the next call.

3. Have a discussion with others about challenging scenarios and what they did or could do to adapt and overcome them. (This adds ideas/mental tools for you to use in the future)

# ACCEPT THE FIREFIGHTER
# CAREER CHALLENGE

# An honorable goal for a firefighter: to leave the fire service better than you found it.

—David J. Soler

## CONTINUE THE HONOR OF THOSE WHO HAVE COME BEFORE US AND ACCEPT THE CHALLENGE BESTOWED ON TODAY'S FIREFIGHTERS.

The firefighter profession is an honorable profession because of what we do and how we do it, but mostly because of those that came before us and built that reputation.

Think about this for a second:

What are your thoughts on politicians? What do you think of the motor vehicle agencies? What do you think of the police? What do you think of car salesmen? All of these professions have built a *reputation* and so has the fire service.

The fire service has a rich history of bravery, trust, honor, caring, and dependability because we, as the fire service, have been there when our communities needed us.

It is our job to continue that legacy, to continue to bring honor to the profession of firefighting and the fire service.

It is our turn to take the baton from those who have come before us. It is time to run the race, and eventually to pass the baton on to the future of the fire service.

Here is my challenge to everyone: *Leave it better than you found it.*

Let us leave the fire service better than we found it. It's a responsibility to do our best and to bring out the best in those around us.

It's a challenge to do the right thing even when nobody is watching. But know this: *someone is always watching.*

It's holding ourselves to a higher standard just because we are the fire and EMS service.

It's about being the hands and feet of our communities and our neighborhoods. In essence, it's love.

We do it for the sole motivation and demonstration of love. Love of the fire service, love of our brother and sister firefighters, love of our neighbor, love of those hurting, love of those who have come before us, and those who will come after us.

There are not too many noble things we can do in life anymore, but one of them is to love our neighbor, and that is what we do as fire and EMS personnel.

So let us take up this challenge today, tomorrow, next week, and next year to continue and contribute to the honor of being a firefighter.

Do the best you can moment by moment, call by call, house cleaning by house cleaning, fire by fire, and EMS call by EMS call, to leave the fire service better than you found it.

Do the small things like being polite to the citizens we come in contact with at the grocery store or inspections, being warm and friendly on what we think could be a mundane EMS call, and also while pouring our knowledge and encouragement into others.

It all matters. It all affects the fire service.

Continue to represent the fire service with honor
and leave the fire service better than you found it.

# THE FIREFIGHTER CAREER CHALLENGE

During 2014, the big craze was the "ALS Ice Bucket Challenge." It was an honorable and fun thing to do, and I am glad it was a success for awareness and funding for that cause.

Here's a thought: what if there was a firefighter challenge? What if in this firefighter challenge, we recorded ourselves on the job for an entire shift and then posted it for the firefighter world to see?

If people watched you on the job, would they be inspired? How do you treat people on your calls? How do you treat your coworkers? How do you treat the citizens? How do you dress? How do you talk? How do you carry yourself?

If I took my camera crew and recorded you on the job, would others be inspired? Would they applaud you? If everyone in the fire service had your attitude, work ethic and moral compass, would the fire service change for the better or worse?

> # If everyone in the fire service had your attitude and work ethnic and moral compass, would the fire service change for the better or worse?
>
> —Firefighter Preplan

I challenge you, and so do all the brother and sister firefighters who have come before you, to work each shift to inspire others. Work as if you are being watched by the rest of the firefighter world and all the future firefighters of the world. Inspire them with your attitude, actions, and behaviors. Show them day in and day out how a great firefighter like yourself does this job and leave an example for them to follow.

Remember: there is someone watching, always. So inspire them with your attitude, actions, and behaviors. When the job gets tough, as it sometimes will, remember the passion and desire you originally had to become a firefighter. Be reminded that right now, there are thousands of people who want your job and are praying to get the opportunity to become a firefighter.

## LAST CALL

Everyone has a last call. Be humbled now because some day your last call will happen. Your career will end. It may be planned or it may be an unplanned circumstance. We may not know when it's going to happen, but it will happen.

Let us treat each call and day as if it was our last. Let us be grateful every day for being a firefighter, because we never know when our last call will be.

## THE FIREFIGHTER CAREER CHALLENGE

Continue to represent the fire service with honor and leave the fire service better than you found it.

# *FIREFIGHTER PREPLAN* BONUS

## THE FIRE SERVICE CAREER

> ### Train hard, but know being a great and respected firefighter is a marathon and not a sprint.
>
> —David J. Soler

The way to approach and train for a sprint race is very different from the way one would train for a marathon. If you train hard, but are training for a sprint when the race is a marathon, you are training to fail.

Having a great firefighting career is very rewarding, and the key thing you should understand is that there are several different stages. It's not a sprint. We cannot learn and experience everything we will need to learn and experience in just a year or two.

To learn all the things we need to learn as firefighters is a huge undertaking. But know that you can be a major contributor and valuable part of the team at all the different stages of your career. So you can have two years of experience and be a respected firefighter for that stage of your career.

Your goal is to be a contributor and a respected team member at whatever stage you are at, then continue on the journey to the next stage of the Firefighter Success Training Diamond.

*How do we move a mountain?* One shovel load at a time.

Having a rewarding fire service career and becoming the best you can be requires taking one shovel load at a time. Do things too fast or take on too much and you will get injured, overwhelmed or burned out. Do it too slowly and you may never finish or achieve your potential.

# 8 PHASES OF THE FIRE SERVICE CAREER

## Fire Career Phase 1

*The "Wow" phase*

This stage is when we are first introduced to the fire service. In this stage, you're putting on the gear, going on calls, using the tools of the trade in training (and hopefully on calls), being around other firefighters, and hearing all the exciting stories.

The excitement of every call is awesome because it's all new, and you have never been on patient-assist or smells-and-bells calls. You're feeling excited and overwhelmed at the same time and maybe even questioning yourself or letting some self-doubt creep in. Can you really do that? Did they just do that? You may also be excited or overwhelmed by the sense of importance and contribution you play in your community.

Everything is just "wow" to us.

## Fire Service Career Phase 2

*The "I do" phase*

This stage is just like my little girl in her 2–4-year-old "I do" phase where she wanted to do everything and show that she could do it. As a second-year firefighter, you've been around a little bit and are seeing the cyclical style of the fire service. You're seeing seasonal calls like motorcycle accidents in the summer, the increase in chimney fires in the winter, etc.

You start to see the pattern and now you think you can do it. You are trying to build your confidence and demonstrate that you belong. For the first two years, everything is so new that even though you are wearing the gear, you may not be a valuable team member yet.

So in this stage, you are out to show them that you can do it and that you belong.

## Fire Service Career Phase 3

*Making the next step*

At this stage you have built up some years of experience and have some decent certifications and training. You have "been around the block."

In this stage, you are faced with the "Am I ready for the next level?" question. Can I be a driver/operator? Am I ready? Am I responsible enough? Can I handle the additional training and certifications needed? This is usually a maturing phase where firefighters learn about how much responsibility they will have as driver/operators and senior-level firefighters.

This stage also includes growing in more advanced firefighting tactics and techniques. For example, in some departments, you'll go from engine firefighting/fire extinguishment (engine work), to truck firefighting/ventilation/search and rescue, etc. (truck work).

## Fire Career Phase 4

*From Firefighter/Officer to Firefighter Specialist*

In this stage, you get the opportunity to learn specialized training and/or work on a specialized unit, such as a rescue squad, HAZMAT team, swift-water rescue, high-angle rescue, rescue team, or you may become subject matter experts in your crew, department, county, state, etc.

Again, the Firefighter Success Training Diamond applies to each specialty, and most specialties have different levels, such as awareness level, technician level, specialist level, etc.

The key in this stage is that you are expanding your skills and abilities to be a more valuable contributor/team member on more specialized calls.

## Fire Career Phase 5

*From "buddy to boss" or from "the back seat to the front seat"*

In this stage, you go from being one of the firefighters to being in charge. You have to learn the difference—and deal with the differences—of being the officer and being in charge. You'll learn about the power and the responsibility that comes with it as well as the loss of camaraderie in some cases.

> Although we won't go into detail on the stages of being an officer, the key thing to understand is that there is a change that you'll have to prepare for and be ready for.
>
> Once you enter these stages, you will still have buddies and camaraderie; however, they will evolve into different relationships. Start looking for others to be buddies who are at your same level. For example, once you become an officer, begin to befriend other officers and share stories with them. They will understand and appreciate it.
>
> As you continue up the ladder, those friendships will most likely come from outside your department. Chiefs and battalion chiefs need to befriend chiefs in other departments so they will have friends at their level to share stories with and get advice from.

### Fire Career Phase 6

*From crew boss to station boss*

This phase consists of going from being a crew boss like a engine lieutenant to the station captain. You are now in charge of the firefighters and other officers. You are responsible for running the station, the equipment, personnel issues, district issues, etc.

## Fire Career Phase 7

*From station boss to battalion boss*

This stage consists of going from a station captain to now being responsible for multiple stations and a larger district area.

## Fire Career Phase 8

*From battalion chief to chief*

This stage consists of going from the fire ground command and leading the troops on the scene to being the administrative chief. Like becoming CEO of the company, your time and energy is focused on running the administrative side of the department and leading the department from that perspective and not just on the fire ground—or maybe not on the fire ground at all, depending on the size of your department.

You'll be responsible for the budget, media, county/city executives, and spend very little time on the fire ground.

---

These are eight phases of the fire service career growth chart. As a firefighter, you decide which stage you are willing to work towards or which stage fits your skills and abilities. There are great and respected firefighters in each stage.

It is not a "whoever gets to the top is the greatest firefighter" type of situation. Each stage requires different skills, abilities, and even some personality traits fit better than others. There are different stages of progression, but by no means is this the process to being great or respected or having a rewarding fire service career.

# ACTION PLAN

1. Whenever you feel overwhelmed, break the plan into smaller tasks and/or extend the deadline for completion.3

# EMS IS HERE TO STAY

## 80% of fire service calls are EMS-related.

—Frustrated firefighter

The emergency medical service is becoming a bigger and bigger part of the fire service. If it's not a part of your department now, it's coming.

Most departments have EMS services and you will find that 80% of calls for the fire service are EMS-related. As the fire service evolves, EMS is getting more and more integrated. As an up-and-coming firefighter, the key you must understand is that EMS is here to stay.

So, although it may not be your number one mission, understand that having an EMS background is important. Becoming an emergency medical technician (EMT) or paramedic is valuable and important, especially if it's not yet required of you.

Many fire departments require us to be either basic life support (BLS)-qualified or advance life support (ALS)-qualified. Nonetheless, it is a great skill set to have and it will help you throughout your career. We can perform better on calls and know how to better help people. We can assist more when needed, versus being ignorant to providing vital care to people—especially some of our own firefighters who get hurt on the fire ground.

I have seen a lot of ALS-qualified personnel become chiefs of fire departments, especially big city fire departments. In fact, if you were to be chief someday, how could you best lead the EMS division if you've never ridden the ambulance and known what it's like? Knowing the pain and pleasure that comes from riding the "box" (ambulance) is something we don't want to miss out on in our career.

Don't hesitate to take EMS classes, get certifications, or ride the ambulance thinking those are things that will prevent you from advancing your fire career. I believe they actually enhance it. I have spent years on the ambulance as an EMT and, although it wasn't something I desired to do, I did get a lot of experience from it and I believe it made me a better firefighter.

# ACTION PLAN

1. Repeat three times: "EMS is here to stay."

2. If you have not ridden on the ambulance, plan to do a ride-along to experience it.

# FIREFIGHTER PREPLAN IMPLEMENTATION: LET'S START BUILDING

As I stated in the introduction, this is firefighter wisdom that has been poured into me and that I have observed throughout the years. This book is meant to pass that wisdom on to you so that you too can become a great and respected firefighter and have a rewarding fire service career.

It doesn't matter what we read, watch or listen to unless we implement it. Change happens when we take action. We can know what to do, but if we don't do it, we won't get the result that we want.

Take the nuggets of wisdom that you like in this book and implement them. I will share an implementation plan for you as a guide. Feel free to use it, modify it, or create your own. The key is to build your plan. Once your plan is built and written down, go to work on implementing it. This is the preparation period or work period. You will be preparing to build your career on a foundation of respect and admiration. You will be doing and implementing more and more of these nuggets, adopting new mindsets, being a slave to new and improved habits, and building your skills. If you take this seriously and apply serious discipline, then greatness and respect will follow you all the days of your fire service career.

## THE APPLE TREE

Keep in mind that it's like planting an apple tree. Let's say the goal is to be a respected firefighter, so the apple in this story will represent that.

274

We have learned about what it takes to grow an apple tree. We learned about the soil it needs and the water and fertilizer it needs and how often it needs to be watered or fertilized.

We have studied its predators and we know what can kill the tree, like certain insects, bugs, or animals. Now, it's time to plant. We plant the seeds for an apple tree.

We water and fertilize it. We make sure to plant it where it has good sunlight exposure. After year one, we have a sprouting tree but no apples. We have put in a tremendous amount of work here but have no fruit. We continue and, again after year two, no apples. Again, we have invested a lot of time and energy, yet no apples.

Should we quit? Is it not working? Is this tree not going to give fruit?

An apple tree takes about five years to give fruit. Then year after year, it will provide you with more and more apples. The first five years are a lot of work and no apples. It takes patience and understanding that the goal you desire takes time to grow and bear fruit.

As you embark on your journey, realize that it will take time to get your result. Be in it for the long haul. Have a long-term view as great and respected firefighters do. You will see results and get compliments before five years, but remember, it takes time to build a reputation and only moments to destroy it.

Just like the apple tree, a lightning storm or hurricane or tornado can come on year five and strike it down. So a reputation can be destroyed quickly after years of hard work doing the right things. Know this and think twice before you decide to take a shortcut or do something unethical. You may be canceling out years of hard work.

# THE *FIREFIGHTER PREPLAN*

1. Write down all your dreams and goals for your firefighter career.
2. Once complete, break them into short (1-year), medium (3–5-years), and long-term deadlines (5+ years)
3. Decide on the top three goals you want to work on.
4. Break your goals into small bite-size steps.
5. Get a mentor and coach (if possible) for the goal and your career.
6. Start implementing the plan.
7. Don't quit, but adapt and overcome.
8. Keep going.
9. Re-read and/or listen to this program again.

**EXAMPLE PLAN:**

I would like to be able to drive the pumper/engine.

Step 1 - Learn the requirements for driving a pumper/engine by _____ (date).

Step 2 - Interview 3 current pumper/engine operators and learn what they did to qualify by _____(date).

Step 3 - Develop a plan based on your research. (Your plan is a series of steps like this one.)

Step 4 - Start working your plan.

Step 5 - Continue working your plan. Stay consistent.

Step 6 - Who else wants to be a pumper/engine driver? Would they like to be a training buddy with me? (Ask 3 others to join a study/ training group with you.)

Step 7 - Get a mentor (someone you connect with who is leading by example and willing to share with you and encourage you).

## HOW TO GET A MENTOR:

Think about who would be a great mentor for this goal. Name five to ten people who you would think would be great mentors for you in this engine/pumper goal. Then seek them out and let them know that you are looking to become a pumper/engine operator and that you were wondering if they would share some ideas and advice with you.

If you are at the same station, see if you can help them with their engine checks/chores. Ask them if they would be willing to teach you when they have time. Ask them if they would mind if you called them or texted them with questions from time to time, but not anything too crazy.

Buy them a gift. It could be coffee, a gift card to a store, or dinner for them and their family. Show that you are serious about learning and that you value and appreciate them and their time.

Don't be disappointed if some individuals you ask say they don't have time or if they blow you off. Just go to the next one. You only need one or two. Some people will not have time or might not be good teachers, although they can do the job very well. So keep moving on to find that mentor.

It's also good to have more than one mentor. That way if you have a question or need some help and the first mentor is not available, you would have a second option.

Step 8 - Never quit. Keep going.

You will have setbacks. You may even feel discouraged. You may fail the driving test or hydraulics test. Don't let that stop you. Many people have failed the test. The key is to not quit. Re-take the test, even if it takes you five times. Don't think about what others say or do. Focus on being your best. Focus on learning and developing the skills and abilities you need. Look for other ways to learn the skills. For example, maybe you need to listen to the content to learn it versus reading it. So, record the content into an audio file on your phone or computer and make it an MP3 or audio file and listen to it while you are working out, doing chores, or commuting. Try something else if that doesn't work. Try something else if that didn't work. Just don't give up. Never quit. Never quit. Never quit.

Step 9 -    Never quit. **Keep going.**

  ▶   List three habits/behaviors you want to build and become a slave to them; such as checking your gear and SCBA the moment you get to the station.

  ▶   Take one or two certification classes each year.

  ▶   Choose one of your textbooks from fire class and read it again. Decide on reading a certain number of pages per day or week.

  ▶   Teach a class. Even if you are new, you can teach others. Practice a skill or learn about something like modern fire behavior and let others know you are willing to teach them as a group so you all can learn and stay sharp. Ask your officer if you can teach a training class or lead a round table discussion on what you are studying.

  ▶   Read articles like those at FirefighterToolbox.com everyday or every other day. Pick something you read and test it and implement it.

  ▶   Set up a fitness program. Make it something you can do the rest of your career. Have it include resistance training, cardio, and stretching. Learn and cook one healthy meal every other week. If you do two per month, then at the end of two years, you will have 48 healthy meals (more than a month's worth of dinners) to eat. This will greatly impact your health and life.

278

## FINALLY

I wish you a very rewarding fire service career. I thank you in advance for working hard on yourself and your fire service career so others may live. May God protect you and bless you and your family.

The best gift you can give me is to refer others to this program. I take your referral as an honor because it shows that you will lend your name and credibility to me and this program. Thank you for your referrals.

The best gift you can give yourself is to use this material and implement it into your fire service career. Taking your skills to the next level will indeed impact the lives of others, and that is noble. That is why we are firefighters and I am grateful for that.

Feel free to reach out to me on Twitter or at FirefighterToolbox.com

David J Soler
Twitter - @_davidjsoler and @FFTBco

Join me biweekly with the Firefighter Toolbox Podcast

# ADDITIONAL RESOURCES

### *Firefighter Preplan* Audio Program

A vital companion to this book that will help to deepen your learning by listening to the information over and over while you are working out, commuting, etc. There is additional bonus material in the audio program to enhance your learning experience.

*Learn more at FirefighterPreplan.com*

### *Firefighter Preplan* Online Training Program

A powerful way to spend time with David as he shares these principles and provides examples and lessons to allow you to adopt the material and become a better firefighter.

*Learn more at FirefighterPreplan.com*

### Firefighter Toolbox Podcast

Listen to the interviews and training that Firefighter Toolbox and David provide on the bi-weekly podcast.

*Learn more at FirefighterToolbox.com/about*

### Firefighter Toolbox 5-Minute Clinics

One-page PDF training documents for study and company trainings.

*FirefighterToolbox.com/5minuteclinic*

## FirefighterToolbox.com

FirefighterToolbox is an online training resource and media for firefighters and officers who want to take their skills to the next level. The purpose of Firefighter Toolbox is to build better firefighters and leaders to positively impact the future of the fire service. Firefighter Toolbox provides high quality online training materials, videos, audios, and more for firefighters and officers to learn from and to share with their crews.

*FirefighterToolbox.com*

## Special Report by Firefighter Toolbox

*THE BIG 5: The 5 biggest mistakes firefighters make and how to avoid them.*

This special report outlines the 5 biggest mistakes firefighters make and how to avoid them.

*FirefighterToolbox.com/Big5*

# SPECIAL THANKS

Throughout my years, there have been so many great and respected firefighters that have poured into me. I am eternally grateful for them. Although I can't fit them all in, I want to share at least some of their names. I also want to say again that we all need the positive influences of others to pour into us. So always be looking to learn and be willing to implement those lessons in your lives.

Thank you to the following fire departments for allowing me to serve and thank you to the members of these departments:

- Ridgefield Park Fire Dept. (Ridgefield Park, NJ)
  - Eng Co #2
  - Truck Co #1
  - Mayor & Fire Commissioner George Fosdick
- City of Troy Fire Dept. (Troy, NY)
- Fallston Vol. Fire Co. (Fallston, MD)
- Joppa- Magnolia Vol. Fire Co (Joppa, MD)
  - House 1 - The Castle
  - House 3 - Fort Hanson
- Bel Air Volunteer Fire Co. (Bel Air, MD)
- Harford County Fire Companies (MD)
- Baltimore County Fire Department (MD)
  - Station 15
  - 96th Recruit Class
  - Capt. Bryan T. Smith, B.C. Charles Tudor, F.S. Brian Smoot, B.C. Lancaster, LT. Jeff Akers, F.A.D.O. Brian Griffin, LT. Eric Cole, LT. William Stump
- All those I have interviewed on the podcast or in private or "off the record."
- All those who have contributed to FirefighterToolbox.com.

Battalion Chief Joe Turner

Captain Bryan T. Smith

Deputy Chief Frank Viscuso

Lieutenant Jim Moss

Captain Rich Gardiner

Fire Apparatus Driver-Operator
Michael Rehfeld

Allison Mosley

Dr. Karlie Moore

Captain Andy Starnes

Assistant Chief Robert Simmons

Chief Robert Fling

Lieutenant John Hayowyk Jr.

Firefighter-Paramedic Buffy Schilling

Captain Erik Wood

Chief Les Karpluk

Division Chief Johnny Winston Jr.

Instructor John Dixon

Captain Rob Cannon

Lieutenant Scott Ebbert

John Gallagher

Brett Dzadik

Sarah Fuhrman

Battalion Chief Josh Fannon

Chief Susanna S. Williams

Assistant Chief Becki White

Deputy Chief Catherine Capriles

Lori Mercer

Battalion Chief Mike Meyers

Battalion Chief Patrick Kenny

Dave Stachowiak, Ed.D.

Joe Starnes KTF

Chief Christopher James

Deputy Chief Stephen Kalman

Instructor Dave Walsh

Battalion Chief Brian P. Kazmierzak

Chief Dennis Rubin

Bill Shanahan

Firefighter/Paramedic Ryan
Pennington

Chief Alan Brunacini

Dr. Denis Onieal

Chief Jim Murphy

Chief Bobby Halton

Captain Mark vonAppen

Captain Thomas Buckley

Captain Bob Farrell

Division Chief Jimm Walsh

Chief Shawn Oke

Instructor Sean Wilson

Firefighter Chris Moren

Instructor Mike Daley

Dr. Rich Gasaway

Lieutenant Rob Ramirez

Division Chief Walt Lewis

Captain Gregory May

Captain Angie Hughes

Firefighter Aaron Zamzow

Captain Jonathan Lusk

Captain Frank Lipski

Captain Eric J. Larson

Lieutenant Mike Champo

Firefighter Shauna Baccus

Christine Sarracino

Phillips Chan

Joe Jurecka, M.S.

Kevin Phillips

Captain Larry Manasco

# ABOUT THE AUTHOR

**D**avid J. Soler has been called to enrich lives and catalyze success. He is a Christian, firefighter, author, podcaster, sought-after speaker, entrepreneur, and the founder/publisher of *Firefighter Toolbox*, which is on a mission to build better firefighters and leaders in the fire service.

He is the host of iTunes top-rated firefighter training podcast called Firefighter Toolbox Podcast. (He has interviewed legends of the fire service like: Chief Brunacini, FDIC Chief Halton, Chief Rubin, NFA Administrator Dr. Oneial, Army Chief of Fire Training Robert Simmons, Deputy Chief and Author Frank Viscuso and so many more.)

In his fire service role, David is known for three things: being a student of great firefighting, training and encouraging up-and-coming firefighters and officers, and sharing firefighter and life success principles.

With over 20 years in the fire service, he is a nationally certified fire instructor III, fire officer II, rescue technician, and HAZMAT technician with experience in both urban and rural fire services. He has served in multiple states as both a career and volunteer firefighter. As a captain, he has led company turnarounds in taking low-responding, low-motivated fire companies and turning them into highly-motivated, top-responding fire companies.

David Soler is a second-generation firefighter and has been a firefighter in several states, including New York, New Jersey, and Maryland.

He is an Eagle Scout and has a bachelor's in management and technology from Rensselaer Polytechnic Institute (NY). He is married and has two daughters.

To learn more about David or becoming a better firefighter and leader, goto FirefighterToolbox.com.

Made in the USA
Middletown, DE
16 December 2018